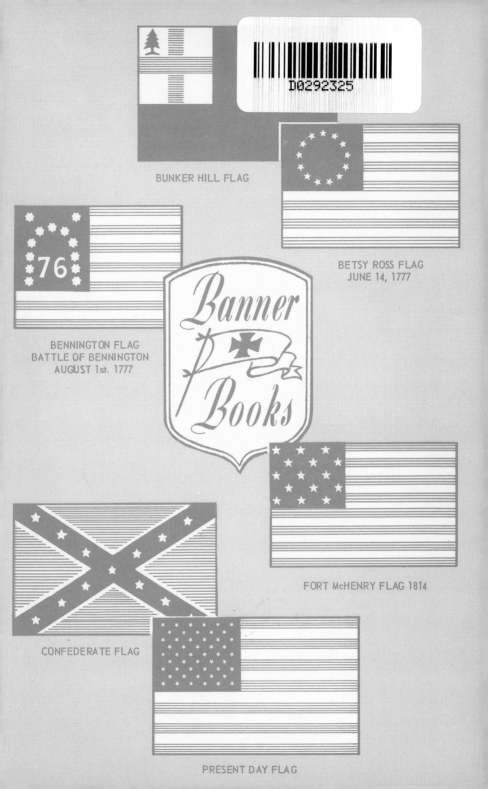

BUNKER HILL FLAG

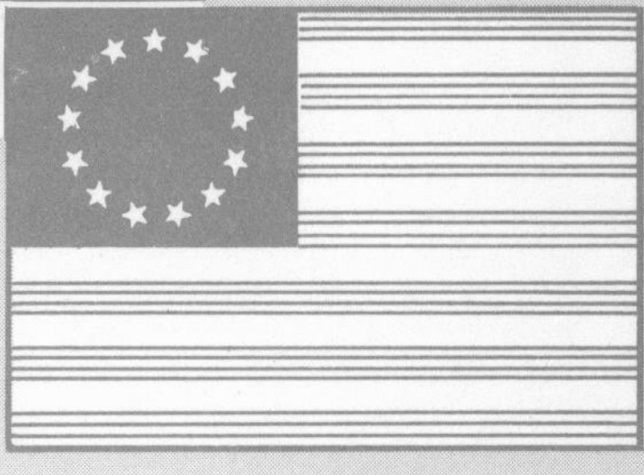

BETSY ROSS FLAG
JUNE 14, 1777

BENNINGTON FLAG
BATTLE OF BENNINGTON
AUGUST 1st. 1777

Banner Books

FORT McHENRY FLAG 1814

CONFEDERATE FLAG

PRESENT DAY FLAG

MOTHER ALFRED
AND
THE DOCTORS MAYO

A BANNER BOOK

MOTHER ALFRED AND THE DOCTORS MAYO

By JAMES P. RICHARDSON

Illustrations by CHARLES DOUGHERTY

BENZIGER BROTHERS, INC.
New York, Boston, Cincinnati, Chicago, San Francisco

NIHIL OBSTAT:

John A. Goodwine, S.T.L., J.C.D.
Censor Librorum

IMPRIMATUR:

✠ Francis Cardinal Spellman
Archbishop of New York
October 5, 1959

The Nihil Obstat and Imprimatur are official declarations that a book or pamphlet is free of doctrinal or moral error. No implication is contained therein that those who have granted the Nihil Obstat and Imprimatur agree with the contents, opinions, or statements expressed.

LIBRARY OF CONGRESS CATALOG CARD NUMBER: 59–15177

CONTENTS

ACKNOWLEDGMENTS

DOCUMENTARY material used in this story of Mother Alfred was supplied by various sources.

Of particular assistance were: Mother M. Callista, General Superior, Sisters of the Third Order Regular of Saint Francis of the Congregation of Our Lady of Lourdes, Rochester, Minnesota; Sister Mary Brigh, administrator, Saint Mary's Hospital; Sister M. Emmanuel, Dean of the College of Saint Teresa (Winona); Sister M. Caedmon and Sister M. Francis Ann, historians; and Sister M. Assisi, Sister M. Florentine, and Sister M. Cornelia, who knew Mother Alfred.

Other data were furnished by the Grand Duchess Carlotta of Luxembourg and her Minister Emeritus of Education, Nicolas Margue; Abbé Ries of Remich; and Holy Cross Father Francis Phelan of Notre Dame, Indiana.

J. P. R.
May 31, 1959

one

TORNADO

"EVERYBODY! Run for the cellar!"

The voice rang out, echoing across the great yard and bouncing off the brick walls around the garden where Mother Alfred shouted as she ran.

"Hurry! Everybody to the cellar!"

Mother Alfred sprinted over the lawn, casting a glance over her shoulder at distant clouds in the dark sky, twisting far above the gray horizon. She came skidding up to the cellar door in a flurry of flying skirts, jangling rosary beads, and spraying stones from the gravel walk under her high-button shoes.

Inside the convent, Sisters ran from the chapel, the parlors, from the hallways, and hurried down the stairways to the cellar. They moved quickly, like soldiers under orders from their general; everybody always obeyed Mother Alfred.

"Sister!" Mother Alfred's voice pierced the gray air again, and the parade of Sisters moving down the steps halted. "Where is Sister Barbara?"

"I got her, Mother. I got everybody!" A sweet little voice sang out in an Irish brogue from the top of the stairs, where a short and stocky Sister was helping an older nun get her footing.

"Good, Sister Gabriel! Now, God bless you, get a move on yourself." Gently Mother Alfred took Sister Barbara by the arm, and guided her down the stairs. Sister Gabriel followed along.

In the cellar, Sisters were kneeling, standing, and walking around. Everyone seemed to know that this was no ordinary prairie storm.

"Everybody over to that corner," Mother Alfred

ordered gently, pointing toward the southwest. "Down on the floor!"

As the Sisters scuffled toward the southwest corner of the cellar, a hot wind blew hard, and the dark skies began to pour rain. The rain splashed like ocean waves against the brick walls, and the little windows of the cellar looked like portholes in a marooned ship. The wind made whistling sounds, louder and louder, until the roars and water drowned out the soft sounds of the Hail Mary as a conventful of Sisters, lying on a cellar floor, recited the Rosary through the terrible storm.

From her position on the floor Sister Gabriel imagined that she felt the brick walls swaying in the drenched wind—

WHROOMPH!

In a crackling flash and a roar, the crashing wind seized the building and shook it fiercely and then veered away again. In that instant, everyone knew.

A TORNADO!

Suddenly the air was heavy with mysterious, awful silence. The Sisters' prayers stopped a moment, stopped in unison, and then started again softly. Sister Gabriel felt funny—it was so still, so frightening; but then she could tell that it was raining again. It was raining hard, and the air felt cooler and wetter and more gloomy.

Sister Gabriel knew that the danger was past, at least for now. She remembered that tornadoes are like giant whirlwinds spinning hundreds of miles an hour. She had seen what other tornadoes had done, smashing buildings, lifting roofs, wrecking almost everything in sight, and sometimes killing people.

But here, in the cellar, everything looked the same as ever. Nobody hurt, no walls knocked down.

Nevertheless, a tornado *had* roared past the convent, *had* spun by like a corkscrew shot out of a cannon, perhaps mere feet away. Now to go upstairs and outside—to see the sights. Sister Gabriel looked at Mother Alfred.

"Wait here," Mother Alfred said calmly. She stood on the first step of the cellar stairs, and called out gently, "Thanks be to God."

"Amen." The women's voices soothed the troubled air.

"Sisters Cornelia, Florentine, Assisi, and you—Sister Gabriel—come with me. All others go with Sister Joseph to the dining room. I am sorry that supper has been delayed this way."

Sister Gabriel caught the twinkle in Mother Alfred's eyes. The placid face, stern and beautiful, was always firm; but Sister Gabriel marvelled that Mother Alfred could joke about a tornado. In a basement full of frightened girls and women there had not been one wail or sob—because Mother Alfred was there.

Under the basement stairway, Sister Gabriel saw Mopsy, Mother Alfred's great Saint Bernard dog. Mopsy's huge jaw was still flat on the floor, as though he was not sure that the storm was really over. "Say, Mopsy," whispered Sister Gabriel, "are you a dog or a scaredy cat?"

But Mopsy did not get the joke. The big Saint Bernard merely raised his large eyes up to Mother Alfred, standing by the stairs. "Get up, Mopsy," she said gently. "Come along and help us. Everything will be all right."

Mopsy followed Mother up the stairs with the Sisters, gingerly at first but not really afraid any more, because Mother Alfred gave courage to everybody—even to a big coward of a dog!

Mother Alfred knew how important Mopsy would be if—God forbid—anyone had been hurt in the storm. Saint Bernard dogs were made for helping people, whether in the windswept Alps or the stormy prairie town of Rochester, Minnesota in 1883.

The first floor of the convent seemed to be all right. Not even a broken window! Mother Alfred, leading the Sisters through the rooms, put her fingers to her lips and whispered, "Hush—" as she cocked an ear toward the second-story stairway. Then she pulled her coif just a tiny way from her head, to hear better. She heard the sound of wind and rain, too close for comfort. "Come along," she commanded softly.

Mother Alfred hurried up the stairs, with Sister Assisi close behind her with a lighted candle. And there it was—a gaping hole at the far corner of the roof, ripped open by the winds. Rain was getting in, too, soaking the beds under the torn roof. Quickly Mother Alfred called for two Sisters to move the beds away from the opening.

"Put up some tenting cloth as best you can," Mother said quietly. "We don't want the floors to warp."

Then she was at a window, peering into the darkness outside. The other Sisters tiptoed up beside her to look, too. Sister Assisi blew out her candle so that they might all see better through the window into the eerie night.

Across the street from the convent, everything looked the same as always—but no! There was a tree broken off, the trunk bare of bark, the tree-top blown away.

And could that be a flagpole, that thing bent over like a hairpin looped to the ground? And the rooftops! Were those buildings over there in the dim light without roofs? Sure enough, whole roofs were gone! But where had they gone? In the dark you couldn't see very much.

"Come along." Mother Alfred almost sailed, skirts billowing, across the slippery polished floor of the dormitory and disappeared into the hallway. Sister Assisi struck a match to light her candle again, while the others followed Mother Alfred.

Grasping the stair-rail, Mother Alfred let herself down the steps in a sort of fast glide; the others trailed her as well as they could in the dark, because Sister Assisi had to lag behind with the candle, moving slowly lest the flickering flame blow out. Downstairs, someone was knocking at the door.

As Mother Alfred reached the foot of the stairs, Sister Joseph was opening the door—to behold a young boy, his shoulders heaving as he gasped for breath.

"Mother Superior!" He swallowed loudly, breathlessly, and in the dim light beads of sweat glistened on his forehead. "Mother Superior. The doc wants Mother

Superior to come right away. Doc—says—people—hurt!" The boy leaned against the doorjamb, exhausted from his run, trying to catch his breath. Mother Alfred went up to him and took his hand.

"Sister Gabriel, get a glass of water. Come in, boy." She led him to a chair in the parlor, and he started talking breathlessly again.

"Doc says—bring a couple Sisters with you. Lots of people hurt." Sister Bridget came running from the kitchen with a glass of water, which the boy gulped down, and then his words came more easily. "Doc says I should just tell you, and you'll know."

"Where is the doctor?"

"Buck Hotel."

"They call that Lower Town."

"Yeah, across the tracks there. North side."

"Is that where the tornado hit the hardest?"

"Everything is wrecked. I saw some dead bodies!" The boy's eyes widened, and new drops of sweat rolled down his summer-tanned cheeks. He was barefoot, and his denim overalls were soaked from his long run in the rain.

Mother Alfred patted his wet arm with her cool white fingers and said softly, "Anything else, boy?"

"My folks weren't hurt. I saw them on my way here." He shuddered, then wriggled his shoulders to shake off the shivers of the chilled night.

"Sister Gabriel, get a wrap, please." Mother Alfred tried to remember if one of the pupils might have left a sweater behind after the past spring term. "And Sister Gabriel," she called out, "make an extra kettle of soup, and coffee and tea, and sandwiches. We may have guests tonight." Then to the boy, "How do you feel now?"

"Okay. I was coming home from fishing when the storm blew up. I ducked into the hotel, and that's where the doc said—"

"He may need you again. Do you want to come along?"

"Sure." He stood up, just as Sister Gabriel handed him a fancy girl's-style sweater. He frowned at it.

"Put it on. Nobody will notice. Let's go. Sister Joseph, bring along Sister Mary Martha. We may need somebody big and strong." And Mother Alfred was out the door, running toward the street, trailed by a barefoot boy in an ill-fitting girlish sweater that he tried to button across his chest as he ran, and a Saint Bernard dog.

And then down the stone steps of the convent came little Sister Joseph and big Sister Mary Martha, taller than Mother Alfred and much broader. She was the jolly red-faced Sister to whom Mother Alfred always gave the "men's jobs," like spading the garden or trundling the wheelbarrow or carrying out the trash barrels. Sister Mary Martha could run, too, and Sister Joseph had to scamper fast to keep ahead of her as they ran in single file down the street.

two

A WRECKED TOWN

MOTHER ALFRED ran smoothly, her head held high, jumping over broken boards that used to be wooden steps and porches, careful not to step on any spikes and nails. She looked like a great goose followed by frightened ducklings, little Sister Joseph and the barefoot boy skimming behind her around piles of wreckage, big Sister Mary Martha and Mopsy bringing up the rear, ready to pick up and carry any of the others who might fall out of this strange race downtown.

They leaped over a dead horse—one, two, three, four—ducked under a twisted lamp-post bent toward the ground, and kept on running.

People stood along the street, men and women and children, looking half-dazed, staring at the rubble, turning their heads slowly as they saw the Sisters run by.

Sister Joseph noticed that the bystanders moved their heads and mumbled as Mother Alfred passed them. Once or twice she heard Mother's clear voice, "Anybody hurt here?" But the headshakes said no.

Suddenly the wreckage seemed worse, heavier, as they ran. Trees lay across the street. Bricks seemed to be scattered everywhere. The runners stumbled, slowed down. Sheets of tin from roofs lay all around. Broken boards, planks, tables, chairs, unrecognizable debris lay

thick on the ground. Sister Mary Martha put her shoulder to an iron fence that the tornado had coiled across the street, blocking the way, but it was imbedded in wreckage and wouldn't budge.

Mother Alfred vaulted the fence and smiled impatiently as Sister Mary Martha lifted the two smaller people over, hoisted Mopsy, and swung across herself. The going got harder then, and the sky seemed to grow darker, but the rain had let up; eventually they got to a wider street with less litter in it.

Here the store buildings had withstood the tornado better than the neighboring houses. And there, far down the wide street, lights shone and people were moving about. At the corner, carriages clustered, horses restless in their harnesses.

"That's it," the boy called out. "That's the Buck Hotel there." People were going in and out, shadows against the yellow light of the hotel lobby. The four ran faster, and Mopsy fell behind.

Mother Alfred darted into the wide, open doorway. There in the foyer, and farther into the lobby, and on the ornate stairway behind the hotel clerk's desk, the injured were lying. They were groaning, crying aloud, gasping. And through a side door came more people, frowning men carrying injured bodies—on boards, in blankets, in their arms.

Mother Alfred's eyes swept the huge room in one long glance. Then she headed straight for the stairway, where a small man was kneeling beside a still body. "Doctor Mayo," she said softly, "I brought the Sisters."

"Good." The little doctor did not look up from his patient, a young girl whose eyes were fixed on the ceiling, trying to bear the pain that was plainly written on her pale face. "This child has a broken leg," he said.

"I brought the boy back with me, too, Doctor Mayo."

"Send him to my office for splints. Doctor Will and

Charlie are there. We'll need more dressings and bandages, too."

"Yes, Doctor." Carefully, Mother Alfred stepped around Doctor Mayo's long frock coattails, which were spread on the floor behind him. He was a short man, hardly taller than the barefoot boy messenger, but stockily built, with strong and straight shoulders. Probably nobody in town except Dr. Mayo's wife, Louise, and his children had ever seen him without his frock coat, the symbol of his medical profession.

"We have no count of the dead yet, Mother, or the casualties. How do things look up in your part of town?"

"Apparently not so bad. Some damage, but we know of no injured."

"Did you bring your dog?"

"Yes."

"Lend him to the searchers. And Mother, we'll need places to care for people. No hospital within a hundred miles, you know." Doctor Mayo kept on working on the little girl's leg as he talked.

"Our home certainly is—"

"Of course, Mother," Doctor Mayo broke in on her. "Of course, I know that. But I sent for you to tell the people personally. They're funny about convents and nuns and the like, you know."

"We can take more than a hundred in the convent, and the schoolrooms are vacant, as well." Mother Alfred glanced around the hotel lobby again, as if counting bodies. She saw Doctor Allen and George Weber, the druggist, busy among the injured. She ran through her mental list of town doctors who must be working like this elsewhere. Doctors Galloway and Sanborn and Westfall and Martin and Cross and Mosse. Doctor Mayo had told her that his sons, Will, a doctor, and Charlie, a medical student, were at his office.

So many doctors—and no hospital in the town—no hospital within a hundred miles! And here were countless dead and dying and suffering people.

"Mother," Doctor Mayo said patiently, "listen carefully."

"Yes, Doctor?"

"Go to the hotelkeeper. Tell him that those who can be moved, on doctors' orders, are to be taken to your house. And say *house*, Mother. Do not say 'convent.' "

"As you say, Doctor."

"Tell him in a loud voice, Mother. Try to have some of the bystanders hear you. Make it sound like both a doctor's order and a general invitation."

"Yes, Doctor."

"Then accompany the first wagon to your convent. Don't stay here. My horse and buggy are outside, I believe." Not once did Doctor Mayo look up.

"We may have to carry the injured on foot, Doctor. Some of the streets will be impassable for a carriage." Mother Alfred looked across the lobby toward Sister Mary Martha, who was kneeling beside a ragged form on the floor, her bulk seeming to hide the injured body from the many others in the big room. But now Doctor Mayo was talking again in a low voice.

"Take a round-about route. The injured cannot be carried such a distance, except by carriage. My horse is good. Find streets that are passable."

"Yes, Doctor." Mother Alfred realized that Doctor Mayo was thinking clearly, with the wonderful cool-headedness of good doctors everywhere. He was not excited. He was not talking loudly, and he was going on with his work every moment as he made plans in this emergency.

"The streets to the south must be all right, Mother."

"Yes." Mother Alfred remembered that tornados usually cut paths not more than a few hundred yards wide. Certainly this was what Doctor Mayo meant. Take a side-street, go along the road behind the convent where the storm had not struck. And if there should be a fallen tree across the road, trust Sister Mary Martha: if she could not move such a tree, perhaps she could lift Doctor Mayo's wagon over it!

"God bless you, Doctor."

Mother Alfred stood up straight, turned toward the hotel lobby desk, and began a fast walk—the same long steps that so many short-legged children and short-winded Sisters knew well. But there were too many people, too many outstretched bodies in the big hotel lobby, and now Mother Alfred had to slow down to make her way more carefully to the big counter desk. As she moved along, she counted perhaps ten faces on the floor, faces with the piercing look of pain. There were other people, too, some moaning or trying to cry, and some looking more frightened than hurt. Mother Alfred tried to see Sister Joseph, but could not. When she arrived at the desk, a tall man with dark wavy moustaches was tearing up a pile of bed sheets into emergency bandages.

"Hello, Sister," he said grimly. "Want some of these?"

"Doctor Mayo was asking for bandages."

"Help yourself. I guess there are some dead, besides," the man said.

"I am Mother Alfred," she told him. "From the Convent of St. Francis."

"Pleased to meet you, Mother Alfred. I am Charles Brown, from New York a month ago."

"How do you do?" Mother Alfred smiled a tiny smile. "Doctor Mayo will be ordering some of the injured people to be taken in his carriage. Let us get his horse ready. We must waste no time. And, Mr. Brown, we need volunteers."

She turned to the group of bystanders who had been staring at this strange sight—a nun in a hotel lobby. "Gentlemen, we need volunteers. Doctor Mayo has ordered that some of the injured be taken to our house." Then she turned back to the desk clerk and said, "Please send anyone who needs food or shelter to our house on Center Street. It is the large red brick house that looks like a school."

Charles Brown nodded and went on folding bandages as a little squad of men followed Mother Alfred across the lobby in the direction of Doctor Mayo. They found him showing some other men how to carry his small patient on an emergency stretcher—a big kitchen door that he had told them to take down off its hinges to use as a flat carrier for people with broken bones.

Doctor Mayo called out, "You men with Mother Alfred, there, clear a path for the bearers. Mother Alfred, watch for fever. If you run out of rubbing alcohol, cold water will help bring down a temperature." Then he turned to attend another patient.

Mother Alfred led the volunteers through the lobby. As they passed the hotel desk, she called out to Charles Brown, "Please tell Sister Joseph that I have gone home and will send Sisters to help her."

He waved goodby and went off to the far side of the great room to find Sister Joseph while Mother Alfred, Sister Mary Martha, and the stretcher-bearers marched toward the doorway and the desolate streets.

three

EMERGENCY NURSE

THE MAN driving the carriage found a clear passage to the convent by avoiding the edge of the wreckage scattered by the tornado. At one street corner, Mother Alfred looked down the block, where lantern lights were flickering, and thought that she saw Mopsy's large head and shoulders bobbing up and down among a group of searchers.

She thought, "Mopsy will see more of the damage and suffering than most of the men will see, but she will not be able to tell anyone about it."

Mother Alfred touched the forehead of her injured passenger. No fever yet.

Minutes went by, and the carriage turned into the drive behind the convent. Mother Alfred blinked to see so many lighted windows. The building was almost aglow with lamp light, and through the rain-washed windows she saw the convent parlors crowded with people, mostly women and children, who had found their way to the shelter of Saint Francis Convent after the storm.

As she led the stretcher-bearers to a second-floor dormitory, Mother Alfred paused on the stairs to look into one of the parlors.

"Just picture it!" A small lady was gesturing helplessly. "Our roof blown away—and not a one of us hurt!"

"The same at our house," said another.

"They say it was even worse downtown," said still another woman. "My husband took us here and then went to see if he could help."

The excited voices faded away as Mother Alfred

continued up the stairs. She chose a bed near a window for the girl with the broken leg.

Carefully, she and two of the men lifted the patient from the door-stretcher to the bed. One of the men asked, "What are those sticks for?"

"Splints," said Mother Alfred. "They hold broken bones in place for proper mending."

"Something new?"

"No. Doctors in Europe used splints centuries ago."

The man pursed his mouth, wonderingly. "When my brother broke his arm, the doctor just wrapped a tight bandage around it," he said.

Mother Alfred nodded. She looked across the dormitory and caught the eye of a Sister who was making up the other beds.

"Yes, Mother?" the Sister asked.

"Sister John, will you please tell Sister Barbara that I would like to see her when she can come up?"

"Yes, Mother." Sister John started for the doorway, but before she had taken more than a few steps Mother Alfred called softly, "Wait—don't have her climb the stairs. Just ask her to play the piano—something cheerful that the people might want to sing together." As Sister John disappeared into the hall, Mother Alfred turned to the two men and said, "I think that you should return to Doctor Mayo." Silently they agreed and turned toward the door as Mother Alfred went on, "Don't forget your stretcher, and God bless you."

Like obedient little boys, they came back and picked

up the kitchen door. Balancing it between them, they began their strange journey into the night, back to the eerie emergency ward in the lobby of the Buck Hotel.

Far away downstairs, a piano sounded, with a faint chorus—"Rain, rain, go away"—and there was a roll of weak laughter from people who had just lost their homes and their possessions in a tornado.

Once again Mother Alfred touched the forehead of her patient. Still no fever, but the little girl was moaning now.

With a sigh, Mother Alfred whispered to the suffering child, "Chéri . . . Mädchen . . . don't cry. Everything will be all right. When you are better we'll go walking in the woods."

The words echoed in Mother Alfred's memory, whispering in a voice both young and old, sometimes in French and sometimes in German. "*Chéri . . . Mädchen* . . . we'll go walking in the woods. . . ."

The spent hours and years of Mother Alfred's life seemed to sweep backwards like hands on a make-believe clock in the misty sky.

In her mind's eye she saw her family home, the house of Pierre-Gerard Moes, the blacksmith. It was a tall cream-colored house across the sea in Luxembourg, in a city called Remich, on the green hills beside the Moselle River. She remembered the gray stone steps and a great front door strapped with iron bands.

The Moes house stood shoulder-to-shoulder with other houses along the rock-paved street, but the ironwork on the door made it stand out. Moes men were metalworkers like their ancestors, and Moes smiths had made most of the hinges and locks and hardware throughout Remich and the countryside.

Behind the great door and up an iron staircase, a girl lay sick in bed, moaning softly. The girl looked like Sister Barbara a half-century ago.

"Chéri . . . Mädchen, the doctor is here."

A little man in a long gray coat was taking medicine from a bag. Then he came toward the bed, smiling at the sick girl.

"You are looking better today."

He poured a few drops of liquid from a bottle into a large silver spoon that held a tiny mound of white powder. He held the spoon to the girl's lips, and she swallowed the medicine.

"Much better today," the doctor said, turning to Mama Moes, who was watching her child helplessly. "I don't think we'll have to worry."

The doctor talked as he put his medicine bottle and powders into his bag and prepared to leave.

"We try not to worry," Mama Moes said.

"Of course," he replied.

"We remember the other times."

"The epidemics, yes." The doctor remembered the cholera of just a few years before, 1832, when the little hospital in Remich was crowded with sick persons, and many died. "But this is not such sickness."

"Thank the Lord."

The doctor went on talking, as if to himself, though the blacksmith's wife listened to him. "We fear cholera when the crops are bad. But now the crops are bountiful—the vines, the wheat, the potatoes." Then he nodded abruptly and said, "Good morning."

In time, the sick child grew stronger and sat in a chair beside a window overlooking the hillside city. She looked down on roofs of red tile and blue slate on the white and yellow houses that surrounded the tower of old Saint Stephen's Church. Remich was a storybook city.

About two thousand years earlier, Roman conquerors had lived there. And over the centuries, warriors from other lands had come to Luxembourg, or "Little Fortress," to do battle and sometimes to stay here on guard at the crossroads of Europe.

To the east, across the silvery Moselle River and at the foot of the hill, lay Germany. To the south, the Moselle divided Luxembourg from France. And to the north and west were Belgium, Holland, and the sea.

Far below, the Moselle shimmered in the sunlight, changing colors like a chameleon. On the waters, flecks of silver and gold and blue and green glistened; and the girl at the bedroom window imagined trout flashing by in the faraway river, pink scales fading into brown fins as they disappeared from view. . . .

"Mother Alfred!" It was Sister John's voice, breaking in upon the memory, shattering the silence of the dormitory in the Convent of Saint Francis in Rochester,

Minnesota. The year was 1883, and outside the windows the sky was dark.

"I am here," Mother Alfred said from the bedside of the girl with a broken leg.

"Mother Alfred, there are men at the door with more people who have been hurt. Where shall we put them?"

"In here," Mother Alfred replied, hurrying toward the doorway. "This will be hospital quarters. The academy section will be for those who are not hurt but need shelter."

The newly-arrived victims were two men and three women. All were conscious; two of them could walk up the stairs to the "hospital quarters," where Mother Alfred assigned one Sister to each injured person.

"Doctor Mayo wants us to watch for temperatures. He said that we may use alcohol or cold water to try to bring down a fever. If we can do this, we may help prevent lockjaw."

Mother Alfred realized that she was not a nurse, that the Sisters who were in Rochester for the summer retreat were teachers—not nurses.

She realized that nobody in the convent could be sure just how badly injured their patients might be, although the bandages on these poor people seemed vaguely to say:

"Hurt arm."

"Bump on the head."

"Bad cut here."

That was all, and it was nothing; but Mother Alfred knew too that the Sisters' business now was to carry out Doctor Mayo's orders and to await further instructions from him.

"Sister John!"

"Yes, Mother Alfred?"

"You may open the academy section for guests who might wish to retire now. There should be room there for everyone."

"Yes, at least for the moment."

"So far Doctor Mayo has sent his injured to us. Unless there are many more to come, we will have no difficulty making room. Please tell Sister Elizabeth to conduct prayers for those Sisters who do not have other duties."

"Yes, Mother Alfred."

"And please send Sister Gabriel here." Mother Alfred turned back to the little emergency ward in the big room. Her first patient, the girl with the broken leg, was moaning again. She seemed to be suffering more than the others. Perhaps they were not as badly hurt. Perhaps—Mother Alfred thought how little she understood of this whole matter. Then she saw Sister Gabriel coming toward her.

"Sister, do we have a supply of alcohol?"

"A small supply, Mother. We have bandages and linens but very little medicine."

Mother Alfred sighed again. "We must not use medicines except as prescribed. We can do nothing but obey doctors' orders."

One fact throbbed through Mother Alfred's mind. Teachers may know many things, but they are not nurses. They were almost helpless in this emergency. It had been the same once before—was it 1866?—in Tennessee, in the epidemic. Two Sisters died among the hundreds who lay suffering with fever. What can people do when they don't know?

"Sister Gabriel, will you get something to make a screen here? We must try to enclose a sleeping area for the Sisters who will need rest."

"Yes, Mother Alfred."

"If we cannot manage here, Sisters may take quarters

in the parlors. I give you complete charge of this duty, but please call if you need help."

As Sister Gabriel left the room, Mother Alfred tiptoed toward the beds where the injured lay. She glanced toward the windows and into the darkness, wondering if perhaps Doctor Mayo might be sending another doctor to the convent. Maybe he would send his son, Doctor Will, or the younger boy, Charlie, who was a medical student and apprentice to the old doctor.

But who knew how many other victims might need the attention of all the doctors in town that night? How many dead? There were a thousand questions, and not one real answer.

four

MEMORIES

THROUGH the night, Mother Alfred sat watch over her little emergency ward. Her single purpose was to carry out Doctor Mayo's instructions. And her Sisters of Saint Francis, well trained in religious obedience, would do only what Mother Alfred told them to do.

But Mother Alfred found herself thinking now and then, as the hours ticked away, of hospitals in France, Germany, in Luxembourg—even in the storybook city of Remich, where a hospital had been standing on the hillside for hundreds of years, waiting for the dread epidemics and sheltering the sick.

The fleeting thought of her homeland almost haunted Mother Alfred. The girl with the broken leg did look as Sister Barbara had looked long ago. Mother Alfred's memory kept returning to the bedroom in Luxembourg where her frail sister, Catherine, now Sister Barbara, had often lain. "Get well, get well," Mother Alfred had often said to her. "Then we shall go walking in the woods."

"Mother Alfred! Can you come downstairs right away?" Sister John was standing beside her, bending low and whispering softly, urgently. "There are many more people arriving, and they may be badly hurt!"

Downstairs, Mother Alfred beheld a terrifying sight. This group of injured persons had not been attended by the doctor! She saw the raw wounds and almost felt the unbandaged pain.

Some of the injured had been carried into the convent and were lying on the floor. Others were trying to remain standing, leaning on each other, all but helpless.

Mother Alfred looked at some of the men who had come in with the wounded and asked, "Who is in charge?" Several of the men looked at each other and shrugged. She spoke to the one nearest her. "Did the doctor send you?"

"We didn't see a doctor," he replied. "We just heard you were taking people, so we brought them here."

Mother Alfred heard herself saying, "We have no doctor here." Suddenly she wheeled toward the other men and asked, "Who is the fastest runner among you?"

Several of the men shook their heads. They had been doing rescue work, digging in wreckage, carrying bodies —hardly knowing what they were doing or where they were going. But one man said, "I guess I could run some more."

"Good. Do you know the Buck Hotel downtown?"

"Yes, Ma'am."

"And you know Doctor Mayo?"

"The old doc?"

"Yes. Now listen carefully. Go to the Buck Hotel, find Doctor Mayo, tell him that we have people here who have not yet been attended by a doctor. Tell him that no doctor has been here."

"Yes, Ma'am." The man started for the door, Mother Alfred following him.

"Ask for Doctor Mayo," she called out after the man. "He will know what to do."

Mother Alfred stood outside the door for a moment, inhaling the night air. Confusion seemed to swell around her, and she wanted to push it away—to think clearly. Then, fingering the rosary beads that hung from her waist, she went inside.

She looked over her latest arrivals and felt more helpless than ever.

"Sister John, Sister Gabriel—please bring cots to the parlor." Mother Alfred looked at one man who was on the floor; she wondered if he could be moved at all. "Sister, will you bring blankets here at once?" Perhaps it would be better to let him stay on the floor until a doctor could see him.

How could she know?

Would her runner find the doctor? Would the doctor be able to come? Perhaps he would send another doctor.

Mother Alfred helped arrange blankets for those on the floor. There was a child who did not seem to be badly hurt but who was whimpering, a man who clenched his teeth silently, a woman with dark skin and straight black hair—an Indian woman whose eyes looked glassy. The Indian woman was moaning.

"You men who are all right," Mother Alfred said, "If you are rested now, perhaps you should go back to see what remains to be done."

One of the men replied slowly, "All right, Ma'am, but it seems awfully disorganized out there." He nodded toward the dark city.

"Yes," Mother Alfred said softly. She tried to put the fact out of her mind. God alone knew how "disorganized" this night had become.

"I hope, Ma'am," the man said, "we didn't do a wrong thing by bringing people here. Someone thought there was a doctor here."

"You did well," Mother Alfred told him gently.

"It was a cyclone, wasn't it?" he asked.

"It seems so," she said wearily.

"I never saw anything like this," he went on, "Not even in the war." Then he turned abruptly toward the door. The others who had helped carry the injured followed him outside, and went away into the night.

Through a parlor doorway, Mother Alfred saw Sister Barbara. "Are you tired?" Sister Barbara shook her head. "If you can, you should get some sleep."

Then Mother Alfred knelt beside the Indian woman, wondering what to do—what to do. Once again fingering her beads, she waited for word from the doctor.

And once again remembered words echoed in Mother Alfred's mind. "I am a teacher," the words said. She could hear her own voice saying, "I came to America to teach Indians!"

The stillness, the moaning, and the waiting crowded in upon Mother Alfred's prayers.

To teach Indians!

That was why she had come to America with her older sister—to teach in the Indian missions.

But it had not worked out that way. Mother Alfred remembered what her father, the Remich blacksmith, had often said.

"The ways of the Lord are unsearchable, my children."

Blacksmith Moes was a powerful man. He could make iron do his will. At his forge in the smithy, drops of sweat that fell from his shiny brow seemed to ring like steel on the anvil. But he knew that his strength, like life itself, was a mystery greater than he could pretend to understand.

One evening long ago, at his dining table with his wife and eight children, Blacksmith Moes had spoken to his family of the mystery which some people call "the future." They listened, Mama Moes and five daughters whom she had taught to work hard, to be thrifty, to be slow to speak and quick to do—and three sons, strong and thoughtful like their father.

At the blacksmith's right hand sat Anton, who had learned the family trade while still a boy. To the father's left was Peter, an apprentice smith, and Joseph, the third son, who liked to work with stone and plaster.

"Our sons and brothers," began Blacksmith Moes, "work at trades as I can teach them and as they can learn from others.

"And our daughters and sisters learn well from their mother. They already can keep house well. But two of my daughters have a gift for studies."

The blacksmith looked wonderingly at Marie, the youngest, and Catherine, his middle-daughter. The other three girls, almost in chorus, said, "We don't want to go to school, Papa."

"I know," he replied. These three wanted husbands, perhaps, and no more. But the other two daughters were scholars. A hardworking blacksmith sometimes can know this as easily as more learned men.

"I think," he said, "we have found a school more suitable than the Luxembourg Normal College where schoolmasters are trained. It is a convent school of the Sisters in Metz. Both daughters may attend there, even though they are seven years apart in age.

"I am not a learned man," he went on. "I do not know the things taught in these schools. I know only one thing that you will find when you are away from our home, and I have decided to tell you now."

"What is that, Papa?"

"In other lands live people who do not believe in God and who do not go to church. This you will learn when you leave Luxembourg."

"We have heard of this," the children agreed.

"It is true," the blacksmith said. "Here everyone is a believer. But not so in other places."

At the convent school in Metz, young ladies learned music, needle arts, the history of other lands, French, and proper German—which was different from the German dialect that Luxembourgers spoke to each other. And at Metz the Moes sisters met people from other nations—even visitors from America.

There was the Bishop Henni from Milwaukee, who told the girls about his work and about other young ladies who had come from Europe to help him. They taught in schools in the new country, and the Bishop called them his "lay apostles," an advanced idea for the year 1842.

The Moes girls read about America, a land of immigrants and descendants of immigrants from all around the world. Luxembourgers, whose country was now peaceful and prosperous, whose people could love each other and believe in God, might not understand why anyone should want to leave home at all. But they could imagine the adventure in journeying across the ocean to a new land!

In America lived Indians, many of them still savages, who must be taught the ways of God-fearing people. What more could lay apostles ask? The thrill of finding such adventure in God's service was something to think about, and the thought came back again and again. A few years later the Moes sisters decided to sail together to America.

But their voyage was delayed for a long time, when Catherine became ill again. Marie Moes waited for her frail older sister to get well enough to set out on the arduous ocean voyage that would take them to America. . . .

The ticking of a clock echoed in the Minnesota night, and suddenly a knock sounded on the convent door. Mother Alfred looked up from the face of the injured Indian woman and sprang toward the door, praying swiftly that Doctor Mayo had got her message.

At the door stood a thin young man wearing a four-in-hand necktie, a gentleman's linen shirt, a store-bought suit of blue serge, and shiny riding boots.

"I wish to see Mother Alfred," he said simply. He seemed very calm and self-confident.

"I am Mother Alfred."

"I am Doctor Will Mayo. My father sent me in response to your message."

"Come in, Doctor." Mother Alfred noticed that he was much taller than his father, this young man in his twenties. He walked unhurriedly behind her as she rushed ahead to the parlor where the injured lay on cots and on the floor. "Right here, Doctor."

"Father is too busy downtown to get away himself."

"Yes, Doctor. These people on the floor and on these cots need attention. There are two others upstairs—besides those whom your father attended and sent here."

"Good. Do you have extra bandages, Mother Alfred? And perhaps two basins of hot water?" He moved from patient to patient, looking at each face carefully. Those who could talk he asked about their injuries; and he carefully felt the limbs and the wrists of those who did not speak. Then he knelt beside the Indian woman and opened his black bag.

It seemed to Mother Alfred that young Doctor Will Mayo worked faster than his father. He did not talk while he wrapped bandages or washed patients' wounds. Mother Alfred stood by with bowls of hot water, wringing cloths as he directed, saying nothing, waiting and watching while young Doctor Will Mayo worked swiftly with bandages and medicines. As she watched, Mother Alfred grew more calm in the doctor's presence.

Then he stood straight and turned to Mother Alfred. "I have done what I can for these," he said in a low voice. "Now perhaps you will let me look over the people upstairs."

"Certainly, Doctor." She led him upstairs, where he made quick rounds of the injured in the beds.

"You are checking for fever?" Doctor Will Mayo asked Mother Alfred.

"The Sisters are watching through the night, Doctor."

"If you do not have alcohol, cold water can help control fevers."

"Yes, Doctor." This was what the elder Doctor Mayo had said downtown. This was the only instructions she had received.

"These emergency conditions are difficult," young Doctor Mayo told Mother Alfred needlessly, but somehow he reassured her as they walked toward the doorway to go downstairs. "We must do the best we can. There are many more injured downtown, and a number are dead. The confusion is considerable," he added.

"I understand, Doctor."

At the door, Doctor Will Mayo bowed slightly toward Mother Alfred. "If you think you need a doctor later, please send another message." Then he was gone.

Mother Alfred stood watching him walk toward his horse, which he mounted expertly. A carriage, she realized, would have slowed his traveling. Then, as his horse's hoofs clattered away into the night, his words echoed for Mother Alfred: "If you think you need a doctor later, please send another message"—he had told her.

"But, young man," Mother Alfred wanted to cry out after him, "how will I know?"

It was a long and horrible night.

five

RELIEF

AT DAYBREAK, Mother Alfred found herself walking from cot to cot, from patient to patient, upstairs and downstairs and up again. To the Sisters who remained awake all night, endlessly touching the foreheads of the patients, pressing wet cloths upon the brows of those who seemed feverish, Mother Alfred repeated:

"If you notice anything that seems especially wrong, tell me at once. The doctor said that we should call him if we think it necessary." The Sisters looked at her anxiously. They knew their Mother Superior, and they wondered at the nervousness of her voice. Mother Alfred fingered her beads and tried to pray.

Shortly after sunrise, the elder Doctor Mayo stood on the convent steps, his frockcoat rumpled, his eyes red. Mother Alfred rushed to open the door while his hand still held the knocker. "Come in, Doctor Mayo."

The old doctor nodded his head toward the horse and carriage in the drive behind him. "Good morning, Mother Superior. Even my horse has had no sleep."

He followed Mother Alfred into the parlors. "How are the patients, Mother Superior?"

"I cannot be sure, of course," she told him.

"I suppose not," he replied wearily.

"However, when your son came last night he seemed satisfied."

The elderly doctor opened his bag, and Mother watched him examine the patients lying side by side. He called one man by name and said hello to several others. And a woman smiled at Doctor Mayo when he bent over her.

Then he turned to Mother Alfred. "These patients look good," he said. "Maybe luck is on our side now."

"Luck, Doctor?" She beckoned him toward the stairs, to take him to the patients in the dormitory.

"Luck," he repeated. "The tornado was bad luck, surely. But luck has a way of turning, I believe."

"You do believe in luck, then, Doctor Mayo?"

The old doctor scowled as he climbed the stairs. Mother Alfred could picture his scowl, though she could not see his face. "A man must believe in something," he said. "How else could anyone go on after a terrible thing like this?"

In the hallway at the top of the stairs, Mother Alfred looked at Doctor Mayo. His face was a mask under his mane of gray hair. She could not know his real thoughts. But she said gently, "The ways of the Lord are unsearchable."

Outside the dormitory door, the old doctor stopped

short. "Yes," he said in a low voice, "this tornado will be called an act of God."

Mother Alfred led the doctor into the dormitory.

"Here, Doctor Mayo," she said quickly, "our first patient last night—the child with the broken leg." They

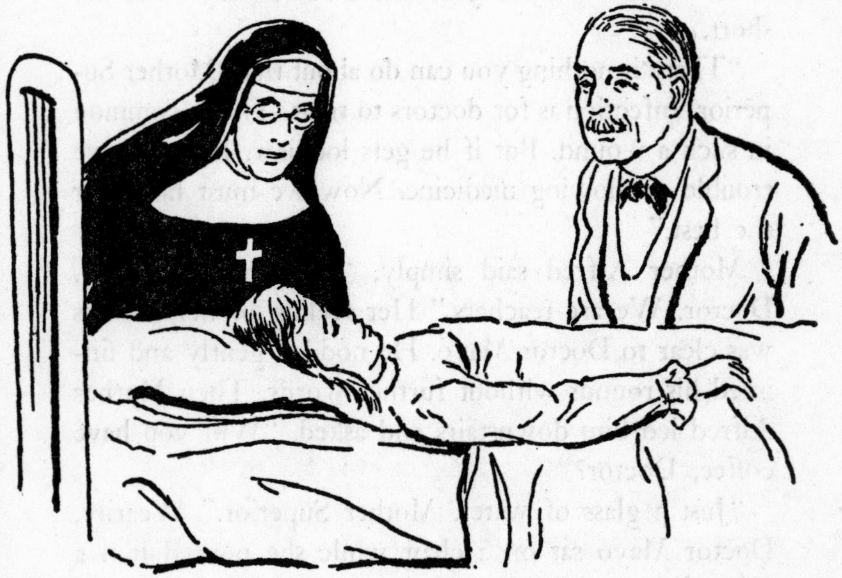

looked at the girl who had lain moaning most of the night.

"I know her parents," he said. "I wonder if their house was hit."

"She fell asleep several hours ago," Mother Alfred told him.

Doctor Mayo touched the girl's forehead. "We must be alert," he said, half to himself. "These injuries may result in more than sleep. Unconsciousness sometimes looks like sleep." He sighed, then turned to the next bed, where a man lay still, his head bandaged, his eyes closed. "He is feverish," the doctor said abruptly.

Mother Alfred caught her breath. "There was no fever when—" she began, but Doctor Mayo cut her short.

"There is nothing you can do about that, Mother Superior. Infection is for doctors to treat. This is common in such a wound. But if he gets lockjaw, he will have trouble swallowing medicine. Now we must hope for the best."

Mother Alfred said simply, "We are not nurses, Doctor. We are teachers." Her feeling of helplessness was clear to Doctor Mayo. He nodded gently and finished his rounds without further words. Then Mother Alfred led him downstairs and asked, "Will you have coffee, Doctor?"

"Just a glass of water, Mother Superior." Wearily, Doctor Mayo sat on a chair while she poured him a glass of water.

"You are very tired, Doctor."

The old doctor looked inquiringly at Mother Alfred. He had been known for a half-dozen years as the "family doctor" to her houseful of Sisters. "And you, Mother Superior, have you had any sleep?"

"I think I dozed a bit through the night," she replied. "I found myself remembering things from long ago, Doctor."

"Yes," he said, "remembering happier times."

"Not always, Doctor. I found myself thinking of the cholera epidemic in Tennessee many years ago. That was a dreadful time."

He looked at his water glass. "Cholera follows the water," he mused. "Along the Mississippi to the other rivers. I suppose you were in one of the river towns."

"Two of our Sisters died."

"They got sick while ministering to others?"

"I believe so. Several other Sisters got sick but survived."

The doctor nodded. "And I suppose all the other citizens in the place jumped on riverboats or ran for the woods."

"We are not to judge," she said.

"No. Poor devils." The old doctor put down his water glass. "Mother Superior, did you know that more than twenty bodies have been found so far—all dead in last night's tornado?"

"Twenty?"

"Or more. And perhaps a hundred badly injured. Several hundreds are homeless—everything wiped out but their lives."

"We have a large number here," Mother Alfred nodded toward the back rooms of the convent. "They are quiet now. I wonder that they are all asleep."

"Shock, perhaps," the doctor muttered. "Some don't know yet if their own people are among the dead." He raised his eyebrows again. "We don't even know the identity of all of our patients here, do we?"

"No, Doctor."

"And there are scores more in a couple of places downtown—as good as strangers. But they've all been attended to, as much as we can do."

Mother Alfred asked, "Is there nobody in full charge downtown, Doctor?"

"The Mayor. And the city council is to meet this morning. We'll set up a temporary hospital downtown and some kind of a relief station." Suddenly he jumped to his feet, as if he had rested too long while work remained to be done.

"Downtown?" Mother Alfred asked.

"Yes. We'll be moving your patients as soon as the new plan is organized."

"But there is room here—and Sisters—."

"You did a good job here, Mother Superior. But a central headquarters downtown will be better than scattering patients and doctors this way. And we will need nurses. Can you keep us supplied with Sisters?"

"I think so, Doctor."

"Good. I'll send ambulance wagons for your patients when the beds are ready downtown. Now you should get some sleep."

When Doctor Mayo had gone, Mother Alfred went directly to the convent chapel. She wanted to talk with Father Riordan when he came to offer Mass to get his approval to send Sisters downtown as "nurses." Inside

He talked with the patients; but Will spoke very little, except to give detailed instructions to the nurses.

Mother Alfred sensed that the patients liked Charlie's friendliness. He seemed somehow more like his father than Will, though Mother Alfred could not say exactly why. Perhaps it was only that he talked more.

From Charlie Mayo, Mother Alfred learned about the girl who had a broken leg and about the feverish victim of lockjaw—and the others who had been at the convent that first night after the tornado. They would soon be going home to their families—or to the members that had survived. The tragedy was spread across many city blocks of Rochester, and God alone knew the total anguish. Did the common sharing of so much grief make the sorrow easier or harder to bear? Mother Alfred wondered, but she could not know.

The newspapers published stories about the tornado's destruction. More than 250 families lost their possessions; 119 homes were smashed to ruins.

Relief money came from neighbor cities. Chicago sent $10,000; St. Paul and Minneapolis sent $5,000 each; Winona and St. Cloud—little cities in Minnesota, like Rochester—each sent $3,000. Little towns held socials and entertainments to raise money for Rochester. As the money came in—more than $75,000—a relief committee distributed the funds to rebuild the destroyed homes and to buy clothing and furniture and building supplies for the destitute families. Over the weeks, Doctor Mayo sent his patients home, one-by-one, until the temporary "hospital" could be closed. Slowly Rochester began to recover from the tornado.

One fact stood sharply in Mother Alfred's mind. The Sisters of Saint Francis had escaped the ravages of the storm, except for a hole in their convent roof.

Workmen were rebuilding houses in the fall sunshine, racing against the approach of winter, and none could be spared now to repair the roof. That had to be covered with canvas, and it served as a reminder to Mother Alfred that she must go downtown one day to see old Doctor Mayo.

For Mother Alfred had an idea.

six

PLANS FOR A HOSPITAL

MOTHER ALFRED'S idea had been suggested to her by someone else. Bishop John Ireland of St. Paul had talked with her about it some months before the tornado.

"Have you thought, Mother Alfred, about building a hospital in Rochester?"

"But we are teachers, Your Excellency," she had replied.

"In St. Paul," the bishop told her, "the Sisters of Saint Joseph have built a good hospital. It is something to think about—a worthy work for any group of Sisters."

The tornado surely had set Mother Alfred thinking about Bishop Ireland's suggestion. Why, she asked herself, was there no hospital in Rochester—no hospital within a hundred miles? Her home town in Luxembourg, little Remich, which was smaller than Rochester, had a hospital two centuries old. She resolved to ask Doctor Mayo about this.

And one day she did. Mother Alfred walked downtown to old Doctor Mayo's office.

"Good afternoon, Mother Superior. You are looking well."

"I am well, thank you, Doctor. I came to talk with you."

"Mother Superior, I recall that we did not have much time when last we talked. Well," the old doctor held a chair for Mother Alfred, "please sit down."

Mother Alfred sat straight on the edge of the chair, facing the doctor. "Yes," she said, "it was after the tornado."

"The people are rebuilding," Doctor Mayo said. "Life goes on."

Mother Alfred looked squarely at the little, gray-haired doctor and asked plainly:

"Doctor Mayo, don't you think a hospital would be an excellent thing for Rochester?"

"It wouldn't work," he replied without hesitation.

"Then, I see, you *have* thought about it."

Doctor Mayo leaned back in his chair. "This town would not support a hospital, Mother Superior."

"Why do you say that?"

He placed his hands together firmly. "Most of the people in this town think of hospitals as pest-houses where people go to die."

"But you know better than that, Doctor."

"Yes, but the people don't feel the need of a hospital until there is an emergency—an epidemic or a disaster."

"They can be taught, Doctor. Think of the great hospitals that have been in Europe for centuries."

"Yes, of course," the doctor said. "Hospitals should be places where people go to get well, to receive the benefits of modern surgery and the best medical care."

"I agree, Doctor."

The doctor leaned forward. "A hospital would cost too much to build," he said firmly. "No, I cannot believe that this would be a good risk. I would not attempt to build a hospital in Rochester."

Mother Alfred looked at Doctor Mayo and said slowly:

"Doctor Mayo, if I build a hospital, will you take charge of it?"

The old doctor turned in his chair and looked out the window of his office. "Mother Superior, perhaps you do not know much of the story of my life."

"I know," Mother Alfred interrupted him, "that you are a good doctor."

"I repeat, Mother Superior, that this town would not support a hospital. Why, there is not a hospital within a hundred miles—that is how much people here think about hospitals."

"Doctor Mayo, the very fact that there is no hospital within a hundred miles means that there is a need for one. People will come from long distances, as they do in Europe, if we have a good hospital. Do you not agree to this much, Doctor?"

He rubbed his moustache thoughtfully. "There is still another objection, Mother Superior. Many of the people in this country do not understand the work of convents and women in religion. Some people fear the priests of your Church. This is foolish, of course, but these things add to the risk of trying to build a hospital in such circumstances as these."

"You sound sure, Doctor, but I too am sure. It can be done."

Doctor Mayo smiled kindly at Mother Alfred. "Mother Superior, let me tell you something of my life. Perhaps you will know then what I mean." He pointed to his microscope. "See this instrument? To buy this I mortgaged my family's house. I am still paying for my previous horse, now dead. We have had panics in recent years—bankruptcies, fortunes lost. And a doctor's income is dependent on people's fortunes, large and small. No, I insist that to build a hospital would be to invite financial disaster."

"But God does provide, Doctor Mayo. The Sisters of Saint Francis will build a hospital. You will risk no money. We trust in God," she said simply.

Then Mother Alfred spoke again. "I have trusted in God," she said, "and we now have teachers in schools and convents from Ohio to Minnesota. In God's care we prosper according to His will and our needs."

"But let me tell you, Mother Alfred! As an old doctor I know how medicine and money go together. Let me tell you of just a few labors I have engaged in—just a few of the things that I have had to do to support my family."

Mother Alfred nodded.

"I came from Europe almost forty years ago, a young man trained in chemistry.

"I came from England, but my ancestors came from Flanders, Belgium, to escape religious persecution. I started working in Bellevue Hospital, in New York, and then I worked my way west.

"In Indiana I ran a tailor's shop. In St. Paul my wife had a millinery store, because medicine would not support our family. I used to journey to New York to buy merchandise for my wife's store.

"I took a job as census-taker of the Lake Superior country—and walked from St. Paul to Superior, Wisconsin. That was a hundred and sixty miles to walk, many times over. And I rowed from Duluth to the Canadian border, taking a census of trappers.

"Later I ran a ferry, was a steamboat officer on the Mississippi, lived through the massacre at New Ulm in 1862, published a newspaper, was a justice of the peace, a farmer and—" Doctor Mayo threw up his arms and looked wearily at Mother Alfred. "All these things because medicine does not pay a living in this frontier country. No, I would not dare risk building a hospital in this town, Mother Superior."

The door of Doctor Mayo's office swung open suddenly, and Mother Alfred saw Doctor Will and young Charlie enter. Will was carrying his doctor's bag, Charlie a black book. Will nodded, and Charlie smiled toward his father and Mother Alfred.

"Father," said Will, "I would like a consultation with you when you have time."

"Certainly," the old doctor replied. "Mother Superior and I will soon be finished."

"If it is urgent, I can wait," Mother Alfred said.

Doctor Mayo stood up. "Young Will went out on a serious case for me," he said. "A lady with a tumor. I do think I should consult with him, with your permission, Mother Superior."

"I will wait." Mother Alfred arose and walked toward the far side of Doctor Mayo's office. She looked out the window into the street, where horses were pulling carts and wagons.

She heard Doctor Mayo and young Doctor Will speaking in low voices at first and then louder. She heard Will tell his father that he would do the operation tomorrow, in the kitchen of the woman's home. Charlie would give the anesthetic—the chloroform. Their father, Doctor Mayo, would be assistant surgeon. Then the two sons were gone, and Doctor Mayo was alone again with Mother Alfred.

"My boys are coming along," the old Doctor said. "Surgery tomorrow, and they made a collection today." He tossed his head toward the desk. "That's what that black book is for, I guess. They write down how much people pay."

"Will your sons make good doctors?" Mother Alfred asked.

"Certainly. I went into debt to send them to medical schools and can never regret it. They are good boys, Mother Superior. I only hope that they will be able to make a living as doctors, without having to be jacks-of-all-trades like their father." Doctor Mayo stared sadly out the windows of his office.

"There is another reason, Doctor Mayo, for you to approve of building a hospital here. Think what it will mean to your boys' future!"

The old doctor nodded agreeably. "The future, yes. Your idea has merit for the future—who knows how many years ahead? But for the present, I must say no.

I do not believe that a slight chance for success should be risked at this time."

"Are there other reasons, Doctor, for your discouragement? Something perhaps that you do not wish to speak of to me?"

"Mother Superior, I believe that we can talk frankly. You are a woman with a fine record of accomplishment; such a record is not made easily. You have struggled many times and have won success. But you have never built a hospital such as you are proposing now."

"That is true, Doctor Mayo. I have never built a hospital of any kind. But I wish to do so, with your help."

"A hospital would be a most difficult undertaking, Mother Superior. There are many obstacles other than the mere building. As I mentioned, your being Catholic sisters would hardly help in this situation."

"Certainly I have considered that, Doctor."

"Some of the people here are not sympathetic to Catholics, as yet, Mother Superior."

"That will come, Doctor."

"Yes, I know that is true, Mother Superior. But I know this region well. You are some years ahead of time."

"But Doctor, your own life and work reassure me that the cause of suffering humanity knows no religion or creed. Doctor, how else could I ask your help?"

"I understand, Mother Superior, and I thank you."

"Furthermore, I am sure that your sons will understand, because you have taught them, and they will thank you, too."

"Mother Superior," Doctor Mayo said sternly, "do you realize what a failure could do to them? And the first hospital in this town easily could result in a failure. This could ruin them before they had a chance to make a living. Do you not agree, Mother Superior?"

Mother Alfred thought a moment before replying. She was not sure that she understood Doctor Mayo's words about his own struggles to "make a living." She knew something about her own struggles to "make a life," but she sensed that the world of religion and convents was vastly different from Doctor Mayo's life. So she spoke gently.

"I have more than a hundred 'children,' Doctor Mayo—my Sisters of Saint Francis. They are all dependent on me, and I am dependent on God's providence. My 'children' will not grow up and leave home, to ease the burden. Instead, I pray that many others will come. In fact, I will never stop seeking others to invite into our convents."

The doctor was staring at Mother Alfred. Slowly he stroked his chin, pursing his lips, deep in thought. Then he said, "Mother, you do amaze me!"

"Many times in my life, Doctor Mayo, I have been without money, without encouragement from others. But never without faith."

"Go on," he said. He began pacing the floor near his desk.

"You told me of the many things that you have done in your life. I have done as many things, myself, though not so exciting perhaps as working as a river pilot and a battle surgeon in the Indian uprising."

"A hospital would serve poor devils who cannot pay," said the doctor. "As a country doctor I know what I know. I got into politics to try to fight the evil forces that ruin people. And yes—sometimes even ruin their health. Broken and ruined, how could sick people who can't work—how could they support a hospital, Mother Superior?"

"I have come to ask you, Doctor Mayo, if you will be chief of staff for a new hospital that I wish to build in Rochester."

Doctor Mayo squinted at Mother Alfred, and the squint became a frown, with shadows of veins showing under the skin of his forehead. Was she merely asking his advice without intending to let him influence her? "Mother Superior," he said gruffly, "even if you could build a hospital here, there is no assurance whatever that it would be a success."

"Very true," Mother Alfred said slowly. "But if you will promise to take charge of it, we will set a hospital before you. I do not wish to begin until I have that assurance from you."

"I see," said Doctor Mayo.

"You will be chief of staff—and your sons surely will benefit from this opportunity."

"Mother Superior," Doctor Mayo replied quickly,

"how much money would the Sisters be willing to spend on this hospital?" He stood facing her.

"How much would you want, Doctor?"

"Would you be willing to risk $40,000?" Doctor Mayo stepped back, expecting the figure to shock Mother Alfred.

"Yes," she said simply. "And more if you want it. All you have to do is draw up the plans and agree to be in charge."

Doctor Mayo sighed. "I see that your mind is made up, Mother Superior. I do hope you are right again."

"With your hope, I am confident," she said. "Doctor Mayo, with our faith, hope, and energy, it will succeed."

"I'll begin preliminary work on some plans, Mother Superior. This will require time—I must warn you." He forced a little smile.

Mother Alfred nodded and stood up to go. Without saying more, she left Doctor Mayo staring out his office window.

seven

HOPES AND TEARS

MOTHER ALFRED was thoughtful as she turned her steps toward home—to the convent. She had not expected Doctor Mayo to try to discourage her. She had asked his advice, expecting him to cry *Bravo!* Yes!

But Doctor Mayo had not agreed with her enthusiastically. Yet, she had over-ruled him—had talked him into something. She was just now beginning to realize this. And her heart pounded at the realization.

At a corner, Mother Alfred turned down the block. She would take "the long way" home, she decided. The walk would help her collect her thoughts.

To the north, far ahead, lay the Zumbro River. To the west were miles of prairie farmlands. She would take a long walk to relax this excitement and to think over her plans.

But why did she feel so excited? Could it be that Doctor Mayo had put doubts into her head—doubts about a hospital and about money and about the future? Why had he told her of his life-long struggles to make a living? Hadn't her own life been filled with struggles? And was struggling any easier for a woman than for a man?

The ground seemed to skim along under Mother Alfred's heavy shoes. Her feet were racing to keep up with her thoughts.

At the river Mother Alfred spied a little path along the shore, leading away from the city. She walked along, watching the sunbeams playing on the water. She glanced behind her, wondering if anyone might be watching her. Mother Alfred sometimes took walks to do errands or shopping, to catch the trains or riverboats or stages that took her on her travels from one town to another, to visit convents or schools in her charge, or to look over the countryside wherever she might be. She had chosen sites for her buildings in this way.

But this was a special walk, she realized. She was taking a walk *to think*. To think about a hospital? To think about gathering forty thousand dollars? She had raised money all her life. It was part of her, to build convents and schools—and to keep them going while she went on building others. And to make them all grow and prosper.

Was it really so hard? Mother Alfred had not always thought so. She had heard priests and bishops say that the Church was growing with the frontier. Mother Alfred had begun by going where there were people, and she had found herself starting schools for the children. Lately she had gone beyond the big settlements, out where settlers were few, and she had built schools for the settlers to fill. She had never really questioned the way that she had lived for so many years and in so many places.

Mother Alfred had come to Minnesota from the East just seven years before, because a priest had asked her to look over his new parish, to see if it were suitable for a new academy. Her bishop back East had been a little like Doctor Mayo. He too had tried to discourage her at first. But in the end the bishop permitted her and twenty-four volunteer Sisters to "start anew" in Minnesota, where settlers were trying to change the forest and sod into cities and farms. Her Sisters were not afraid of hard work or of adventure in God's service.

They had opened their Academy of the Sacred Heart in Owatonna, in 1877; and the same year they opened the Academy of Our Lady of Lourdes in Rochester. Other cities wanted schools—and Sisters to teach in them. Mother Alfred had trained numerous Sisters, had staffed dozens of schools at the bidding of priests and bishops, some of whom did not seem to understand the details of raising money, which to Mother Alfred simply meant pinching pennies.

She knew that some people did not fully understand how to raise money; someone else had to do it for them. Furthermore, Mother Alfred knew something about the power of faith—as well as the "hope and energy" she had mentioned to Doctor Mayo. Perhaps if the doctor's faith were different, he could have been more optimistic about a hospital. But she had seen enough of his devotion to fellow human beings to know this man's worth. She had seen him get things done when nobody else could do them.

As the sun flickered on the rippling river, Mother Alfred looked toward the opposite shore. Just a half-century ago, there had been savages here. But even in the few years that Marie and Catherine Moes had delayed in coming to America—the Indians had moved away. America was always changing, always growing, always moving.

Mother Alfred slowed her pace as the path led her toward a clump of trees at the riverbank. She saw a large rock and decided to sit down there by the river, shaded by the trees. She would be alone, and here she would see grain fields and gardens, and farm animals grazing.

This was part of Mother Alfred's hope. The farmers had prosperity. Newspaper editors called the rich crops "bonanzas," as if jealous of the farmers' quick wealth. Mother Alfred knew that towns like Rochester drew their trade from these rich farms, rich because the soil was both fertile and fallow—new land that probably never would be worn out. She knew that success resulted from good farming, from hard work and good sense, just as tragedy could result from foolishness.

These Minnesota towns were built to serve the successful farmers, the homesteaders who had got their properity by working for it, just as Mother Alfred planned to get her hospital by working for it. Whole new towns, with their hotels and blacksmith shops and stores, were like year-around fairgrounds where farmers did their trading. Now railroads were connecting the towns and the new marketplaces. This was the way America was growing, Mother Alfred knew. Why didn't Doctor Mayo realize this? Was it because he was in the midst of it, seeing it all, taking it for granted?

Mother Alfred, busy in her convent, running her system of schools and Sisters in five midwestern states, was able to watch this new American scene from a better distance than the actors who were daily taking part in the drama. She had traveled west behind the frontier, an immigrant on that faint edge of civilization that followed the pioneers.

Her academies and "select schools" that taught French and German and music and needle art were what the newly prosperous people wanted. They wanted an education for their children. And Mother Alfred, equipped to give them the best of European and American culture and to preserve their religious traditions in this wild new land, had been there—even before the railroads.

By 1883, in Southern Minnesota, the bonanza wheat crops were carried to new mills by new locomotives on new railroads. The new Americans in this rich land spent great sums of money—for new houses, new machinery, new luxuries, new entertainments.

The new Americans, Mother Alfred told herself, were generous souls—but some were not thrifty. In bank failures and panics, some were caught unprepared. Even Doctor Mayo was in debt for his home and his medical equipment—and for a horse long dead! This, Mother Alfred knew, was not her way. Her way was to save thriftily, to save everything that could be used, to set aside money in the little amounts that her Sisters earned as teachers, until she had gathered enough to build her new schools and convents.

Was this why she was not afraid of debt? Was this the difference between her courage and Doctor Mayo's?

She looked up. The sun on the Zumbro was gone. The water was dark under gray clouds that were now hiding the sun. For a moment she accused herself of wasting time, of being idle, dreaming of days gone by while she sat by the river!

But she had not been wasting time, she told herself. Just to think of the years past, of the pleasant times and of the hardships, had made her feel better. Now she would return to the convent and get back to business as usual.

Mother Alfred took one last look at the little river. What fun it would be, she thought, to skip a flat stone across the water. But there wasn't a little stone in sight. She decided to take a shortcut back to the convent by cutting across a meadow to a road that she knew came into town from the west. Those clouds were still hiding the sun.

The road's wagon ruts reminded Mother Alfred of other roads that she remembered as far back as Luxembourg . . . Luxembourg . . . Luxembourg. The past echoed through her mind. She could not explain it. For years she had hardly remembered her youth.

And there had always been so much to do—so much work ahead—that she had seldom taken time to dwell upon the past. There had been a new world that needed her work, a new language to learn, more children to teach than she could imagine, and always the need for more Sisters and more schools and more convents and more work. "To think is to do," said others about Mother Alfred.

Nobody ever said, "To think is to rest and dream about the past."

Why were her thoughts today so full of dreams of the past? she wondered. Doctor Mayo's words of discouragement and caution came and went in her mind as she walked along the rutted road.

"It wouldn't work. This town wouldn't support a hospital."

That was what was troubling her. She had over-ruled the doctor's judgment about a hospital. With her mind made up, she had over-ruled one whose wisdom she had dared to trust—the one she had chosen to plan her hospital and to be its chief of staff!

Lightning flashed across the sky, and Mother Alfred looked up to see bright streaks against the dark horizon, streaks that reminded her of the veins that showed in Doctor Mayo's forehead when he frowned. Then came peals of thunder.

Mother Alfred whirled around, scanning the landscape for some kind of shelter. The air smelled damp. There were many trees, from little cottonwoods to big oaks, with thick tops to ward off rain for a time. But Mother Alfred did not want to be under a tall tree in a lightning storm. Mother Alfred started to run ahead along the road, to see what else might present itself. And thunder rumbled again, farther away.

As she ran, she looked over her shoulder, glancing across the sky. No funnel cloud. This would not be a tornado. Just a thunder storm on the prairie.

To the left, beyond a rising knoll, Mother Alfred saw a haystack and a barn. Raindrops began to fall upon her brown wool robes, flapping about her feet, and she increased her speed—dashing as fast as she could toward the barn.

The rain fell harder, and now Mother Alfred's run was uphill; but the barn door was open and, as she flung herself inside, the rain that had been chasing her started to splash harmlessly on the barn roof. She caught her breath and looked about her stormy refuge. Whose barn, whose farm might this be?

Mother Alfred looked about the barn. Surely the horses would not care that she had come there to get out of the rain, which fell harder and faster on the barn roof. More lightning and more thunder rent the sky. Mother Alfred knew that she would be going nowhere until the storm passed. She felt her wet veil and decided that it would dry well enough on her head and shoulders. Her heavy rough shoes were muddy, but water had not soaked through the thick soles; her feet were dry. The coarse wool of her robes was wet on the outside, but she felt comfortable. It was good to have found shelter.

As the rain droned on, Mother Alfred found a milking stool and sat on it. What can a Mother Superior, caught in a rainstorm in a strange barn, do while she waits? She can pray, Mother Alfred knew, and now she fingered her beads again, to pray and to think and to wait.

eight

VOICES FROM THE PAST

"FORGIVE us our trespasses." Mother Alfred smiled to think that she was trespassing even now as she waited in the barn for the rain to subside. Long ago in Luxembourg she and her sister Catherine had "trespassed" so harmlessly. They had been walking with their brother Joseph past an orchard. As they approached the orchard gate, plum blossoms burst upon their sight, and they opened the gate and went into the orchard to sniff the orange-veined flowers.

When they heard someone coming, they ran, and Catherine was the last one out. The orchardkeeper heard her struggle to catch her breath and discovered them. "Why are you children trespassing here?" he scolded.

The little sister spoke quickly. "Please, sir, let our brother talk for us. He will do better than our sister who is weak and out of breath from running to your gate."

The Luxembourg orchardkeeper had looked at Joseph, who was tall as any man. Then he exclaimed, "Are you not children of Pierre-Gerard Moes?"

They all nodded. The man scratched his chin and muttered, "Surely I should not be scolding the iron-worker's children."

"We will tell Papa," the little sister said, "that—"

"But I have not scolded you yet," the man interrupted.

"We will tell him that we trespassed in your orchard—and that you were civil to us," Joseph told him.

The orchardkeeper laughed. "Was I?" he asked.

"Yes," Joseph replied. "And we are sorry for trespassing. We should have asked permission to come near the fruit blossoms."

"Come," the man smiled. "Please come sniff to your hearts' content. Try all the blossoms in the orchard!"

Later, on their way homeward, Joseph said gently, "You are clever, Little One, to ask the orchardkeeper to talk to your brother."

"Big brothers are to protect their sisters," Marie said simply. "Papa told me."

Catherine smiled, too, but she tried not to show it. "I wonder if it is good," she mused aloud, "to be both clever and proud."

"Ah," laughed Joseph. "Blessed are the peacemakers, are they not?" And so the children smiled together, remembering the stern orchardkeeper.

Whenever Papa Moes heard of these things, he would discuss them while seated with his family around the great dining-room table at home.

"The orchardkeeper who spoke to several of my

children has told me how Joseph was made to do the talking for two of my daughters."

"Did we not tell you, Papa? The orchardkeeper was civil to us, and we told you."

"Surely, but not in the way that he told me." The blacksmith's face broke into a slow smile. "But I knew which daughters he was not speaking of." He turned to Margaret and Marie. These daughters, like their mother, usually said little. To them he said, "I know that you two are tired of your classes in the Remich school."

Margaret and Marie nodded. There was no denying this.

"I suppose," Blacksmith Moes went on, "that you would like to be married some day and have homes of your own. Well, now, hear this! Iron ore has been found under the orchardkeeper's land. This discovery may bring riches to many Luxembourgers. You may find very rich husbands—or perhaps large dowries."

"Dowries, Papa?" Margaret and Marie exchanged glances.

Marie interrupted, words bursting from her mouth. "New metal should help a blacksmith prosper too." Then she realized that she had spoken out of turn.

Her mother said slowly, "Marie, you answered for your father."

The blacksmith slapped his leg. "But her answer was exactly right. Such a brainy little one!" he cried, shaking his head in wonder. Then he caught a look from his usually silent wife.

It said: "Do not flatter the child."

Quickly the blacksmith straightened his face and looked sternly at his large hands spread now on the dining room table. "Of course," he said, "we must guard against cleverness. Sometimes people can be too clever for their own good."

"How is this, Papa?"

"For example, there are those who say they do not believe in God. Many of them have gone to schools. Perhaps they studied the wrong things."

"Are they savages," Marie asked, "who have never heard of God?"

"No. Sometimes they have heard of Him but do not believe."

Marie was looking carefully at her father. He seemed troubled, and he seldom spoke this way to his children. Perhaps she could cheer him up a little. "Papa, I feel that these people *must* believe in God."

"Perhaps so, my child." There were some things that Blacksmith Moes did not try to decide for his youngest daughter.

One of the things that he knew she must decide for herself was her life's work. It was the same with Catherine. They wanted to teach Indians in America. This they had discovered at the Sisters' boarding school in Metz. The blacksmith knew that they had talked too of becoming Sisters—since the first year that they had gone away to school.

The blacksmith realized that he had two daughters

whose minds might work very differently from his, and he accepted the differences without questioning them. How else could he permit his two beloved daughters to leave Luxembourg, to sail to America alone?

Over the years, because of Catherine's illness, the plans had been set back and changed so often that the departure somehow did not seem real when finally it was announced in 1851.

But it was real, at last; it was time for good-by to Luxembourg!

There was a "last" time for everything when the day approached. There was a last Sunday in church and a last special blessing from the pastor of Saint Stephen's. There was a last toast with wine, a toast to the success of the voyage and the new life across the sea. There was a last walk through the winding lanes to the fairyland woods and a last look at the beloved river. And then the last night at home with the family.

Sadness mingled with joy! Good-by to dear ones, good-morning to the morrow. The decision had been made, and now they must leave. Luxembourgers knew how to mix sadness with joy. They held a celebration.

Down the streets of Remich, an orchestra marched to the Moes house. Horns blared, drums rolled, music swelled upon the air. Singers shouted in chorus until Blacksmith Moes opened the great door of his house. Then the musicians and the singers went in for a last handshake and good wish, loud and jolly.

And now the good-by was official.

It would last until the Moes girls were down the road and out of sight, bound for their port and America.

The journey to Paris was made by stage, and then by river steamer down the Seine to Le Havre. The ocean voyage meant a sailing-ship, dependent on wind and weather, and the two sisters had to await word that the day was right for sailing.

And eventually it was.

Then, as the captains of a half dozen waiting vessels gave orders to cast loose into the favorable winds and tides, a ship's cannon boomed. Some people cheered, some cried out, some wept. Still, to be in motion was a relief for everyone; and passengers began to dance upon the swaying decks.

Later, hardly anyone could recall the moment that the horizon of Europe disappeared from view, leaving each shipload of passengers surrounded by water and wonder—and dreams of America. What would it be like?

The passengers began leaving their cabins to go up on the deck. From the rail, the Moes sisters looked across the water at their neighbors in the near-by ships. They saw men and women and children, grouped together like families at a festival.

Whole families leaving their native lands?

"Marie, your arm! I feel faint!" Catherine Moes grasped her young sister's arm and silently slipped to the deck of the ship, where she lay still.

"Help!" shouted Marie. "My sister has fainted!" But Catherine revived quickly and sat up on the deck as a man in a frock coat stepped toward them, carrying a chair.

"I am a doctor," he said, "Doctor Schwartz. Do you feel ill?"

"I—I'll be all right," Catherine replied. She let the gallant doctor help her into the chair he had brought across the deck.

"You are traveling alone?" The doctor asked.

"My sister and I are together," Catherine told him. "We are daughters of Pierre-Gerard Moes from Luxembourg."

Dr. Schwartz looked at Marie and nodded. "I see." He stroked his chin thoughtfully and went on, "Forgive my questions. But as a doctor I am concerned about your sister's health." He turned again to Catherine and said kindly, "Tell me, do you feel faint now?"

"I don't think so," she replied.

Marie spoke up. "My sister sometimes tires more easily than I, Doctor."

"And often faints?"

"Not often."

"I see." The doctor smiled at Catherine.

Marie spoke again. "My sister often gets over-excited."

"Over-excited?"

"Yes. More excited than I."

"I see." The doctor asked Catherine, "Do you feel excited now?"

"I think so. I think I did before I—before I felt faint."

Doctor Schwartz continued to stroke his chin. "Mmmm," he mumbled. "Well, no doubt the days aboard ship will grow dull in time. And then you should feel less excited."

"Grow dull?" Marie heard herself cry out.

"Yes," said the doctor. "Miss Moes, is this your first ocean voyage to America?"

"My sister and I have never been abroad," she said.

"So! And where will you visit?"

"We are going to stay. Our destination is Milwaukee."

"To stay!" exclaimed Doctor Schwartz. "I am merely going for a visit myself. For perhaps a year. But if I were going forever—well, I don't wonder that you are excited." He tipped his hat and bowed to the Moes sisters.

"Thank you for your kindness, Doctor Schwartz." Marie really did not want their new acquaintance to go away. She too wondered about Catherine's fainting, and she felt that Doctor Schwartz understood both illness and loneliness. "We do appreciate your kindness to us, Doctor Schwartz," Catherine reassured him.

The doctor nodded silently and joined them in their watch across the water. He understood. Then he said softly, staring at the other sailing ships that had left port with theirs, "Our neighbors are like you, I think. They too are going to America to stay."

"How do you know this, Doctor?"

"Those are immigrant ships. Whole families are sailing away from their homes forever, going to a new land."

"We noticed the families," Marie said.

"Yes," Doctor Schwartz went on. "That seems to be the way of the new country. Americans are from many lands. Whole families move there at once. This is an amazing thing—almost unheard of in history."

"You have been to America, Doctor?"

"Several times," he said. "I have friends in Pennsylvania."

"You did not wish to stay for longer than a visit?"

"No. I prefer Europe. But," Doctor Schwartz added hurriedly, looking at Catherine Moes, "you may prefer the new country. Many people do, you know."

"But why not everyone? Is it good or not?"

"It is different," Doctor Schwartz sighed. "There is a newness in America that troubles me."

"Tell us about this." Both Catherine and Marie were looking eagerly at their new friend.

"America is different from Europe, even though some of the people and the customs may seem to be European. No, I find America new and different and somehow strange for me."

"Go on." They looked at each other again, eagerly.

"Then," the doctor said gently, "look again at our neighbors over there." He pointed toward the other sailing ships. "Consider any of them—perhaps a peasant family who left their farm, perhaps a tradesman who has sold his family's possessions. They must begin new homes in a new land."

"Think of the adventure!" Marie cried.

"I cannot," said Catherine, shaking her head slowly. "I can think only of the danger." She smiled weakly at Doctor Schwartz, as if to assure him that she did not plan to faint again.

"The danger," he said absently, "I had not thought about."

"Nor I," mumbled Marie, leaning over the rail into the sea breeze. She didn't want to talk about danger. What was there to fear if God wanted souls saved? "We trust in God," she said.

"Yes," replied Doctor Schwartz. "The Americans say, 'In God we trust.' " He smiled now at Catherine.

"That is an official American motto, I believe. Perhaps there is no other way to live in a new country." He stared quietly at the miles of ocean.

"Please, Doctor," Marie asked him, "do tell us about the happy things you found in America." She wanted to change the glum mood.

"O-ho," he chuckled. "There are parades and festivals and fireworks on the Fourth of July. And let me tell you—."

The voyage required twenty-seven days, in which time the Moes sisters came to know Doctor Schwartz well. He was German, but he did not love the Prussians who lived next-door to Luxembourg and who had not long before billeted troops in the little country. Furthermore, Doctor Schwartz told them, there were more Irish and English in America than Germans and Luxembourgers.

Doctor Schwartz spent many hours explaining what he knew of the "immigration" to America. The people from nations around the world could become Americans forever, he said—citizens of the United States.

And Indians? The doctor introduced Marie and Catherine to the ship's captain to ask his advice about Indians. "They have moved westward to the Dakotas," the captain said.

"Is Milwaukee in the Dakotas?"

"Milwaukee is a city this side of the Dakotas. You won't have to worry about Indians. The tribes have moved beyond Milwaukee."

Worry about Indians! The sisters were going to America to teach Indians!

The ship docked at New York, and Doctor Schwartz offered to accompany the sisters by train to Philadelphia and by stage to Pittsburgh, which was his destination. From there, he said, they could go to Lake Erie and board an Upper Lakes steamer bound for Milwaukee.

On the wharves in New York they heard new sounds, new shouts, new words. The officials who admitted them, the passersby in the noisy streets, the hotelkeepers and the ticket-takers spoke a strange language. This was not the English that they remembered from their classrooms at the convent school in Metz. The words, most of them, were familiar. But the meanings were not clear. Eagerly they thanked Doctor Schwartz for helping them.

The railroad fare from New York to Philadelphia was four dollars per passenger. Did they know how much four dollars might be? Doctor Schwartz took care of exchanging their foreign money for dollars and seemed surprised when he saw Marie's purse. "Be careful," he said, "not to show how much money you have."

"We have heard of robbers," Marie told him, "and will be careful."

"Not only robbers," he replied, helpless that he could not explain everything that he felt about the strangeness of the new country.

"The money is part of our inheritance," they told

him. "Our family may send us more in installments later, as our father and brothers prosper."

The stage, over plank roads from Philadelphia to Pittsburgh, cost $37, including meals at wayside inns. And the cabin passage to the port of Milwaukee was twelve dollars. Years later Mother Alfred often thanked her patron saints for Doctor Schwartz, whom the sisters never saw again.

And in a way, she liked to think of Catherine's fainting illness as a blessing.

nine

IN THE NEW WORLD

WHEN at last the two immigrants from Luxembourg arrived in Milwaukee in February of 1851, they were welcomed joyously by the bishop. He remembered how interested the girls were when he talked to them at their school at Metz. He sent them to lodge at a nearby convent, where they were greeted by a very tall School Sister of Notre Dame. She announced that she was the Sister Superior.

"We wish to teach Indians," Marie said simply.

"You are speaking French. Do you speak Indian tongues? Chippewa? Sioux?"

"We can learn," replied Marie.

"Indians learn English rather quickly. Do you know English well?"

"No." Marie thought that Catherine appeared to tremble.

"*C'est dommage!*" exclaimed the Sister Superior. "That is a shame." She clucked her tongue softly. "This may be a problem."

"The bishop did not seem concerned about this," Marie said. "He did not speak to us in English."

"Of course not," the Sister Superior smiled. "I am sure that he is as delighted as can be—that you have come all the way from Luxembourg to report to him after almost ten years."

"And he did not say that we cannot teach Indians," Marie said sharply. "I did not even think to ask him, since this was his suggestion when he spoke to us in Europe."

The nun thought a moment. "This is an unusual situation," she said, looking from Catherine to Marie and then back to Catherine again. "We have a number of schools—but no Indian missions. The Indian schools are in Dakota, to the west. The frontier has moved away very rapidly in the past few years."

"I see," said Marie. "But we could go to Dakota, could we not?"

The nun frowned. "There would be difficulties. You see, as the frontier has moved, boundaries have changed, bishops have been changed. It is difficult enough for Sisters who come from a convent," the woman said sadly, "but for young lay women like yourselves—" she shrugged her shoulders. "No, I cannot recommend it now."

Marie looked at her older sister, who was biting her lip nervously. "What do you think?" Marie asked Catherine.

"I do not know what to think," Catherine said. "It seems that we misunderstood."

Again the nun frowned. "No, I do not think so. You have come to do missionary work, and there is missionary work to be done. Do not be deceived by appearances. Some people call our academies 'select schools' because we teach children of prosperous families, but some of our schools are in smaller cities where people are very poor."

Marie sighed. "You use words like 'prosperous' and 'poor.' We know these words, of course, but cannot be sure of their meaning in our new surroundings. In Luxembourg we never saw a beggar. Not everyone is rich, but everyone has enough. Of course," Marie put her hands to her cheeks and closed her eyes, "everything is much more expensive here, we find."

The nun smiled. "Which of you has charge of your purse?" she asked.

Marie looked at Catherine, who nodded silently. Then Marie said, "We share our funds, but I have charge of expenses."

"I thought so," the nun said. "You do seem to do the talking."

"The voyage was sometimes difficult for my sister," Marie said. "I can spare her this extra worry if I keep the purse."

"Yes, of course," the nun agreed.

"But we make all of our decisions together," the

younger sister went on. "It has been this way as long as I can remember."

The nun frowned again. "Time is saved," she said, "when decisions are made by one person. Even in this new country, people govern themselves by choosing a leader."

Now Catherine held her hands to her face, covering her eyes, and Marie asked gently, "Has your headache come back, Catherine?"

"Yes."

"Would you like medicine for it?" Marie asked.

"In a moment—." Suddenly Catherine's hands slipped from her face, which was now whitened, and her eyes shut.

"She has fainted!" cried the nun, jumping from her chair and running around the desk to kneel beside the girl slumped down in the guest's chair. But Marie was already rubbing her older sister's hands, and soon Catherine opened her eyes.

"Don't worry," the younger sister said firmly. "This is merely a fainting spell."

"Does this happen often?" the nun asked.

"No." Marie smiled, seeing that Catherine was reviving well.

The nun persisted. "Do *you* also have headaches or fainting spells?" she asked Marie.

"Never."

The nun sat down again and looked sternly at Marie. "May I make a suggestion, Miss Moes?"

"Certainly, Sister Superior."

"I suggest that you and your sister make an agreement."

"Yes?"

"You are the younger," the Sister Superior said to Marie, "but your sister's health does not seem strong. I suggest that from now on you agree that the younger sister make the decisions."

"But Catherine is the older—" Marie began, until Catherine interrupted her.

"Please, Marie," Catherine said weakly. "Sister Superior has good advice. Let us do as she suggests."

Marie raised an eyebrow and looked at both her older sister and the older nun. They were not telling her what to do—but they were telling her that *she* should decide what to do. Did this make sense? Marie shrugged and replied slowly, "As you say, but I do not like it."

"You must," the nun said gently.

"But don't you see? Even this decision was not mine."

"I do see," the nun told her softly. "I suggest that you decide to stay here with us, at least while you are mastering English and until you get settled. That will be a start for you."

Catherine smiled feebly at Marie. "Let us stay here then," she said. "I will feel better if we do this, until we make other plans."

"If it will make you feel better," Marie agreed. And somehow she felt relieved herself.

The Sister Superior stood up. "I will call a Sister to take you to your quarters," she said. "We will assign you to classes with the other students. They may seem a bit younger than you, but we'll manage."

Through a hall of arches that smelled of strong soap, Marie and Catherine Moes followed the young Sister assigned to them. They went past a statue of the Blessed Virgin, and into a new corridor. Then the Sister came to a halt and turned to them. "You will sleep here," she said to Marie, indicating the doorway of a little alcove. Inside was a bed, a washstand, a chair, and a small window. "The bell will ring for dinner," the Sister said. Then she was gone, leading Catherine down the hall.

Marie tiptoed into the hallway to look after them. Down the hall she saw the Sister stop and gesture—and with that Catherine disappeared into a doorway. Then the Sister walked back along the hall past Marie's alcove, and on down the corridor.

Marie thought a moment. The next thing to worry about seemed to be dinner—and no worry was necessary, really, because somebody else would ring the dinner bell.

Marie sat on the bed, then on the chair, then on the bed again. Then she jumped up and went down the long hall to find Catherine. As she passed other alcoves, all alike, she noticed other girls. Most of them seemed surprised to see her, but nobody said hello.

Marie kept on walking, peering into alcoves until she spied Catherine sitting on a bed, holding her head in her hands. Marie ran to her. "Another headache, Catherine?"

"No. I feel tired but well." Catherine looked at Marie wanly.

"I'll stay with you, anyway," Marie said. "Well, shall we get ready for dinner?" She walked to the washstand and poured water from the pitcher into the basin. "I certainly welcome the chance to wash my face at last."

When the dinner bell rang, the halls seemed to come alive with young women in a sort of parade. Marie and Catherine watched them file by and joined the lines.

Soon they smelled food, the warm smell of kitchens, and presently they were in the dining room.

It was a large high-ceilinged room with rows of long tables. The young women took places behind the rows of chairs, and Marie and Catherine did the same. Then the room was silent as everyone waited in place.

The windows of the dining room were tall and narrow, with sills that began halfway up the walls. Twilight sun streaked into the room through the high windows.

Across the table, other young women stood motionless. They were dressed alike, all wearing plain black dresses with white linen collars and cuffs and short black veils. On a platform above the tables and at the far end of the room sat a nun. A crucifix stood on a little table in front of her. The crucifix seemed to Marie the only decoration in the big dining room; but she resisted the temptation to look around to see what else might be in sight in this silent hall. Suddenly a tinkling bell sounded from the platform, and Marie saw the nun's hand outstretched to a little bell on the table before her.

Immediately the jingling of the bell was drowned out by voices bursting upon the stillness. Then the voices stopped, and the young women behind their chairs made the Sign of the Cross, pulled back their chairs, and sat down to the sound of scraping chairs and women's voices—talking, chattering, laughing gaily.

Marie looked at Catherine as they sat down with the

others. Their glances met in a moment of understanding as they strained to understand the English that was being spoken all around them.

They listened. Perhaps these were the "American dialects" they had heard about. Many of the words were understandable—"very well"—"not very well"—"thank you." But when many English words were strung together rapidly, neither Marie nor Catherine could be sure what this chattery tabletalk really meant.

They knew that the Sister Superior was right. They must study English before they did anything else.

Quietly, Marie and Catherine ate their food—meat, potatoes, and vegetables, one of which they had never seen before but which they learned later was creamed corn—and asparagus, bread, coffee, strawberries. The dinner tasted good, and both Marie and Catherine ate all of their portions.

The young women across the table from them, and on either side, introduced themselves to Marie and Catherine. They asked friendly questions, too, and gave the Moes sisters dozens of warm smiles—but the newcomers from Luxembourg could not understand one word out of ten. So they repeated their names and added "de Luxembourg" and returned the smiles. The dinner was indeed a bewildering pleasure.

Then the nun's little bell jingled again from the platform, and silence came over the dining hall. And, as if upon an unseen signal, the women in the dining hall pushed back from the tables and stood up, rearranging their chairs neatly in rows in front of them.

The bell tinkled again, the Sister on the platform stood up, and the women made the Sign of the Cross and prayed together. Their words again sounded strange, but it was clear that this was their thanksgiving after their meal. And then they crossed themselves once more and fell silent.

Once more the bell tinkled, and the women turned from their places to file out of the dining room as they had come in. They walked in silence, in orderly lines, through the doorway of the big room and into the scrubbed hall. One by one they turned into their alcoves, each under her archway. Catherine went into hers, peeking cautiously to be sure that she remembered the proper alcove and assured when she spied her cotton bag upon the bed.

Marie continued along the hall to her own doorway, and then she heard a voice speak behind her. She recognized the French, clear as a song:

"Sister Superior will see you in her office. Follow me."

Quickly Marie skipped to keep up with the Sister who had spoken to her and who was already walking ahead of her toward the far end of the hall. Marie cast a glance over her shoulder, back down the hall, to see if Catherine were coming, too. There was nobody in sight.

The Sister Superior stood up when Marie entered the office. She smiled and said in French, "The dinner was good?"

"Yes." Marie smiled, too. It was good to hear again words that she understood. "But my sister and I did not understand the conversation, and I fear that we did not meet anyone very well."

The Sister Superior looked at her solemnly. "I must tell you something most seriously," she began. "Let us sit down. There. This is better. I find that I have acted hastily. I believe that your sister's fainting spell upset me more than I realized. I think that is why I suggested so abruptly that you stay here with us in this way—without even introducing you and your sister to our other young women."

"So?" murmured Marie. What could this mean?

"I find," said the Sister Superior, "that I must present your case for admission to our Mother General. She is out of the city, of course, so this will mean a delay. But of course your papers will have to be checked, and arrangements would have to be made for your expenses here. The time will be well used."

"I do not understand," Marie said slowly.

"I will explain. It is agreeable to me that you and your sister stay here now. You are older than our other girls, but since you must learn English and review your studies, this should not matter. However, the rules of our convent declare that your admission must be approved formally by the Mother General. Do you see?"

"Not precisely," Marie replied.

"There is a reason for the rule," the Sister Superior said. "Some of the young women with whom you had dinner are *candidates*, as we call those who have expressed a wish to become Sisters. If all goes well for them, in God's time they may enter our novitiate to prepare for life in the convent."

"You mean," Marie said, "that they are students—but studying for the sisterhood."

"That is correct. Of course, all of them will not persevere. This would seem," she said slowly, looking directly at Marie, "God's way and His will."

"Yes, of course." Marie leaned forward in her chair. "You see," she said in a low voice, thinking that she must choose her words carefully, "my sister Catherine and I have thought of this."

"I understand." The older woman folded her hands against the coarse cloth of her robe and waited for the young immigrant girl to continue. But Marie was silent, her thoughts, her secrets. Then the Sister Superior said gently, "Perhaps you would prefer to speak in German."

"*Bitte, bitte sehr*—if you please," replied Marie. German words were easier for her. Luxembourgers favored German, even in the native patois dialect. Yes, Marie thought, I do prefer German, though I went to a French school.

"Then speak as you wish," said the Sister Superior. "You understand that we School Sisters of Notre Dame are trained in French. That does not matter." She smiled again at young Marie, who knew that the heart of the Sister Superior was gentle because she had given her heart to Our Lord.

"My sister Catherine," began Marie Moes, "has wanted to be Christ's bride since I can remember. Through all of her illnesses, she has waited patiently and has always prayed that He might permit her to become a Sister."

"And you?"

"I too have prayed," Marie whispered, "for my sister and for myself. When we were together at school in France, we agreed that we wished to be Sisters. Then we heard of the Indians in America—from Bishop Henni—and made plans to come here to instruct them."

"Did you tell the bishop at the time that you wished to become nuns?"

"No. That was almost ten years ago, in 1842. Catherine's health was uncertain, and the bishop spoke of lay apostles. We understood that we could journey to America and teach as lay women. But always we thought about becoming Sisters some day."

"That seems a good way," said the Sister Superior. "If you had entered a convent in Europe, you might never have been sent to America."

"Exactly," Marie said excitedly. "That is what our pastor at Saint Stephen's in Remich told us. Oh, it is good that you understand this!"

"But almost ten years have passed."

"True," Marie nodded. "We told our parents and they gave us their blessing. Papa arranged our inheritance to be paid in installments. And we made plans to sail. You will see that our baptismal certificates were first copied in 1846. But Catherine became ill again—time and again—until last year, when she seemed well enough for the voyage."

"What did you do in these years of waiting?"

"Prayed—and worked as a governess," Marie replied. "Catherine went to the new baths at Mondorf in Luxembourg. They were discovered there when workmen drilled a deep well to find salt beds. There under the deepest well in the world they struck warm springs of mineral waters, and Mondorf became a great health resort. Doctors established themselves there, and people came from all over Europe to get well.

"Catherine spent much of her time at Mondorf. Eventually she became strong again. I took a position as a governess at Reisdorf and waited."

The Sister Superior spoke slowly. "Then you really left your family home in Remich some years ago." She smiled again. "This must explain your own confidence and self-assurance. As for Catherine, I thought perhaps she might be suffering from homesickness. I wondered if this might explain her fainting. Of course, I am not a nurse. I am, by training, a teacher."

"Catherine's fainting apparently results from excitement," Marie said. "A doctor on shipboard seemed to agree with this."

"She has fainted that recently?" The Sister Superior tapped her fingers together.

"We were excited about sailing to America," Marie said. "Don't you think this could cause the fainting?"

"I do not know. If you stay here, and if the Mother General approves, there will be time for both you and Catherine to make your decisions. God is good. In His time He will show us His will."

"And we must learn English," Marie said anxiously. "Whether here or elsewhere, we must learn English now."

"With Mother General's approval," smiled the Sister Superior, "you will learn other things. For example, you will be taught to make your bed a certain way." With a twinkle she began folding imaginary bedding, stopping the movements of her hands in midair to see that Marie was watching closely. "Always like this," the Sister Superior said, slapping an imaginary bed, "always so."

Marie nodded happily. She remembered the convent school in Metz and the happy times there. And here in Milwaukee she had found a Sister Superior who could turn from sternness and seriousness to a bit of happy fun. She knew that she would have to make her bed "just so" —but that she could be happy doing it.

"You will have duties," the Sister Superior said. "But now it is the recreation hour. Let us go with your sister to walk in the garden. You can meet the candidates, and perhaps I can help translate a little—from your German and French to their English."

And, as it turned out, Marie need never have worried about receiving the Mother General's permission to stay. Marie and Catherine Moes lived with the School Sisters of Notre Dame for three years. They learned English and they learned how to teach in American schools.

ten

THE TEACHER

BY 1854, Marie and Catherine Moes had been trained to teach music, languages, needle arts, and the classical studies in American finishing schools. They were also ready to teach in English, the language of their new country.

But Marie could not forget that she had come from Luxembourg to teach Indians. One day she asked Sister Superior, "Is our neighboring state called 'Indiana' because Indians live there?"

"Indians once were the only inhabitants of this country. But times have changed very rapidly. The Indians who remain are peaceful."

"Are they Christians?"

"Missionaries may have visited them either here or farther eastward, where they lived years ago."

"I wish that I could go to teach them," Marie said.

The older woman spoke slowly, "If our superiors tell us to visit Indian villages, we obey," she said. "If not, we always remember our lessons about obedience."

Marie stared at her shoes. "I understand, Sister Superior."

"Even if you do not always agree, you must obey," the older woman said gently, a smile beginning in her eyes. "What if you should some day be a Sister Superior?"

Marie was very serious. "I do not think that I would wish that," she said. "My sister Catherine is seven years older than I. We will be together, and I think that she should be my superior."

The two women looked at each other, the wise Sister Superior and the young girl from Luxembourg who had been studying English in the convent. It was clear that Marie still regarded herself as the "little sister." Had these years of study been wasted? The Sister Superior wondered.

When, some time later, the Moes girls announced their wish to go to Indiana, to join the Holy Cross Sisters at Notre Dame, the Sister Superior did not seem surprised. She helped them apply to Notre Dame.

On her application blank, Marie wrote (in the space marked "Reasons for Applying"), "Upon praying I felt called here."

Catherine wrote, "To serve God and instruct youth." Neither mentioned, "To teach Indians." All they asked now was to be Sisters of Holy Cross. For their dowry they gave the Sisters the money remaining from the first installment of their inheritance.

Indiana did prove to have some Indians. As soon as

Marie had received the name "Sister Alfred" and Catherine had become "Sister Barbara," they were sent on short missions to teach catechism. And as they passed through tiny villages and camps along the wagon roads of Indiana they saw Indians. These Indians did not look savage, but they looked poor. Sister Alfred and Sister Barbara wondered if these Indians knew about God and His divine Son.

Their new Sister Superior realized that Sister Alfred and Sister Barbara had exceptional educations. They could teach almost any subject and in three languages—English, German, and French. Even before they made their profession of vows, Sister Barbara was sent to Chicago, to teach German and religion there in Saint Joseph's School for Girls.

"How do you feel about it?" The younger sister tried to speak calmly, to hide her own excitement and worry about the separation.

"I feel happy," her older sister replied. "I have been praying. Now, everything seems well."

In 1858, Sister Alfred and Sister Barbara were together again, teaching school at LaPorte, Indiana. In these years, they were able to study the new country first-hand, to see for themselves some of the things that they had heard about for so long. Their first impressions of America, they knew, had been gathered hastily while they rushed from New York to the West and while they studied English in the convent.

Most of all they were aware of the newness of the

parishes and churches and schools—from Chicago to the little cities in Indiana. Back in Remich, St. Stephen's Church was older than anyone living could remember. Some of the old abbey churches in Luxembourg had

stood for centuries. And even the chapel in the Milwaukee convent had been fashioned in European style.

But here in the bustling Indiana towns, some churches looked almost like sheds. They smelled of green wood, and they seemed always to be the wrong size for the congregations. The Sisters taught school in church basements or in the big "halls" erected next-door to the church buildings by hurried carpenters.

Sometimes churches were mere streets apart—one for the "Irish" parishioners and another for the "German." Now the Moes' ancestral language came in handy, to help the Sisters with children who were as handicapped in this new land as Marie and Catherine had been just a few years before. Sometimes the English-speaking children made fun of the "foreigners."

One day the Irish pastor spoke of this to Sister Alfred. "Sister," he began in his Irish brogue, "it is of your favors that I have been hearing."

"What is this, Father?" The Irish priest's words were as difficult to understand as any others she had heard.

"Your favors for the little Dutch children."

"I don't understand, Father."

"Come now, Sister. Haven't ye been favoring the ones whose German tongue ye speak naturally?" The priest's grin covered his Irish face from ear to ear, but Sister Alfred did not like to be accused of favoring German children. She simply helped them talk.

"Father, I do not believe that I favor anyone. But if you mean what happened to Hans Schultz—."

"What did happen, Sister?"

"John O'Brien and the others were abusing Hans, calling him 'foreigner' and worse names. I made them stop."

The priest shrugged his shoulders. "These things are not unusual, are they?"

"I do not like cruelty, Father. I must teach the children to understand."

"It cannot be done in one day, Sister."

The words of the Sister Superior in Milwaukee, the advice about obedience, echoed in Sister Alfred's mind. "Yes, Father," she said. "I will try to overlook the injustices, if you say that I should."

If Sister Alfred had been the pastor, John O'Brien and anyone else who abused immigrant children would have been punished twice—once for the wrong and again for complaining to the priest. But, just as she learned to obey the pastor, Sister Alfred learned that immigrants from older countries were often "picked on" by those who spoke native English or who had lived longer in the United States.

And she could see why this happened. The immigrants were outnumbered in most groups. In America there were three English or Irish for every German person. For every Frenchman there were at least ten others. And as Sister Alfred watched her schoolchildren form gangs in the play yards, she wondered if she had not really come to America to teach "savages" after all.

At the end of the school term, Sister Alfred and Sister Barbara and the other "German" sisters were sent to a new school in St. John, Indiana. If life in the new world seemed strange to immigrant sisters, the duties were simple: "Obey the superiors."

Sister Alfred studied the new world around her. In Remich, she had seldom seen a stranger; but in America her life seemed to change almost constantly. Here there were new faces in schoolrooms, on the streets, in shops, faces that she had never seen before.

She realized that this was so for other people, too, for whole populations that had come from other towns and farms to find new neighbors, new teachers, new houses and buildings—and new ideas.

There was the time that one of her pupils told her that strict nuns were like "Whigs."

"Nuns are like Whigs?"

"My father says Whigs have always been bossy."

"Your father must be a Democrat."

"He drives a team of horses."

She learned by listening. In the schoolyard she heard a boy say, "My old man got drunk. We're moving to the next town. We've got to get out." In Remich, she had never heard of such a thing. But in America, she learned, people often moved away from troubles to "make a new start." Was this the reason that some immigrant families moved across an ocean—families seeking a "promised land" in a new world, searching for happiness by moving, moving, moving?

In the past year, Sister Alfred had heard that the country was suffering its greatest "panic" in ten years. The stock market had fallen, banks had closed, people's savings were lost, men were out of work. Sister Alfred noticed that the food on the convent table was more meager now. A neighborhood baker brought in gift loaves of bread, a farmer some dried vegetables from his cellar. And the Sisters shared the food with children who came to class hungry.

Sister Alfred now saw the wisdom of her superiors. The Sisters could not give their full energies to teach poor Indians unless there were some sources of income in parishes. The Sisters had to spend their hours teaching for their small earnings.

Because the Sisters were good teachers and worked for small salaries, the school district at near-by Turkey Creek requested Sister Alfred and Sister Barbara to teach there in the district school. They learned to ride horses and rode to Turkey Creek every day. If God wanted them to ride horses, they rode.

When the Sister Superior visited St. John, Sister Alfred mentioned that she rode horseback through an Indian village on the way to Turkey Creek. The Sister Superior sighed, "If only we were able to do all the things that could be done, Sister Alfred!"

"Several girls in the district school have asked me about becoming Sisters. They are interested in our life, Sister Superior."

"There are difficulties, Sister Alfred. Our rules are made by the Motherhouse in France, at LeMans."

Sister Alfred did not say what she was thinking: "I wonder if the Motherhouse in France is too far away from Indiana." Aloud she said: "I came from Europe, and I see many differences between American life and the ways of my native land."

"It is true, Sister Alfred, that some American girls

who apply for admission to our convent are not acceptable to the Motherhouse in France. I do not advise you to encourage young girls to think that they can become Sisters easily. The Motherhouse in France must decide if they are to be encouraged—not us."

Sister Alfred learned many lessons in this way, by silently accepting the rules of her new life. To the boy who had said that his father got drunk, she pleaded, "Do not tell others of your father's troubles. Try to help him, and let us pray for each other." Then she said good-by to the boy, and he joined the misty parade led by Doctor Schwartz, the Sister Superior in Milwaukee, and all the other friends she expected never to see again on this earth.

The children who stayed after school hours puzzled Sister Alfred. Did they enjoy dusting benches? Slowly Sister Alfred realized that they were hungry for the apples that she gave them. The children sometimes told her of their miseries at home, and in their sweet love and trust she found tears to wash away her own cares and thoughts about her home across the sea.

One child told her anxiously, "Jimmy says I am 'teacher's pet.'" The little one was near tears. "He says only pets stay after school to help Sisters."

"He must be teasing." Sister Alfred winced to see that the child was ready to blurt out more woes.

"Sister, is it true that Irish people are lazy?"

"Posh. Who says such a thing?"

"I heard it. And I heard that German people are

stingy and stubborn." The child's eyes begged for assurance.

"Nonsense," Sister Alfred said. From the pocket deep in the folds of her skirt, she took an apple and gave it to the tearful child. She wanted to hold the youngster in her arms. Instead, Sister Alfred grabbed a dustcloth. "Here, let's get busy." She began wiping windowsills furiously, talking to the child about housekeeping. But Sister Alfred's mind wandered back to Remich, where nobody was poor.

Then, as the months went by, Sister Alfred thought she noticed another "change in the times." Some children left school because their fathers had found work in new places to the west. There seemed to be more food, even at the convent, and the children gained weight.

The boys played marching games, pretending to be soldiers in step with imaginary military buglers. They made brassy horn-like noises with fingers pressed to their mouths. The war-like games made Sister Alfred shudder.

Sister Alfred had nothing to worry about. The superior provided what was necessary—or God did—and all Sister Alfred had to do was obey.

In 1859, President James Buchanan declared that the country was prosperous again, that the hardships following the "panic of 1857" were to be forgotten. New pupils came to the school in St. John, and other sisters took up the horseback rides to the "jobs" in Turkey Creek.

The pastor, Father Rachor, gave Sister Alfred a new duty—to teach classes in American history and "to bring it up to date."

"American history is being made every day," Sister Alfred told her pupils. "Some day children will read in their history classes about events that are going on right now."

Meanwhile she read newspapers and books that came her way. Some of the ideas in them seemed sensible to her. She agreed with writers who called unemployment "a waste of labor and of brains." She agreed that extravagance was a wasteful fault.

Other ideas made her wonder. Some Americans wanted a homestead law—to give farms to families who would move west and build homes on land provided by the government. Sister Alfred wondered if the government should encourage this moving, moving, westward, but she knew, too, that people needed homes, needed work, needed hope.

She became interested in the writings of Horace Greeley before she learned that he was a "Whig" and might be as unpopular with some people as "strict nuns" could be with naughty children. She told herself that she agreed with Greeley that "youth should be a season of instruction in industry and the useful arts as well as in the letters and the sciences."

Sister Alfred learned that Americans were in disagreement about many matters:

Should public funds be granted for private and church schools?

What about states' rights, protective tariffs, national banks?

And what about slavery? The country was in a turmoil over slavery. Should the Negro slaves be freed? Famous men like Senator Stephen Douglas and Abraham Lincoln debated, and thousands of Americans came to hear the arguments.

Women seemed to oppose slavery. Men seemed more worried about what might happen if Negro slaves were turned loose in the North to work for cheaper wages than the white men wanted. Perhaps men were not so tender-hearted as women. Sister Alfred could only wonder.

She saw Americans grouping together into "associations"—to abolish slavery, to cry out for public health, for women's rights, for laws against child labor, and even for easier divorce laws. There were torchlight parades for political candidates, campaign songs, crowds that came to picnics arranged for speeches, "camp grounds" where thousands of men and women and children sat and listened.

Associations, banding together, is an American way to get things done, thought Sister Alfred.

She read the news when Congress forbade slavery in the Northwest Territory—and permitted it elsewhere. This changed her history lessons, because two years earlier the Supreme Court had over-ruled the Congress on slavery laws. The people and their leaders could argue that this or that idea was "unconstitutional," but what did it really mean? And she began to realize that men did not agree on the meaning of their nation's Constitution!

In 1860, the Democrats could not agree among themselves—and neither could the Whigs. Each party split in two. Some of the Whigs in the North joined with the Republicans. Others formed a new party, the Constitutional Unionists. These disagreements meant that four parties were now nominating candidates for the presidency of the United States.

Lincoln, a Republican, wanted to give free homesteads to people who would move west, and he opposed slavery in the new territories.

Democrat Douglas said he would let the voters decide if they wanted slavery or not.

Southern Democrat John Breckinridge declared that slavery must be permitted in the territories and protected by the United States government.

"New Party" candidate John Bell avoided the question of slavery and called for voters to support the Constitution, the Union, and "the law."

In the election, Lincoln won, although his three opponents together received a million more votes from the people than he did. But Lincoln's electoral votes made him president, lawfully elected under the Constitution. Now, wondered Sister Alfred, what will the government do about slavery?

But even before Lincoln was inaugurated, South Carolina and six other Southern states withdrew from the United States. Lincoln insisted that the Constitution forbade any state to secede from the Union.

Sister Alfred did not believe there would be a Civil War, but war came . . . eleven Southern states against twenty-three states in the North. Now what would the future bring to Indiana?

It brought the grimness of war.

One day in 1863, Sister Alfred, Sister Barbara, and Sister Bernard stood in the kitchen of their convent, talking.

"Prices are terribly high," Sister Alfred said. "Merchants tell me this war is causing shortages of goods in the stores. Business and farming are going ahead well, but the prices are climbing fast."

"Will the war never end?" asked Sister Bernard.

"The Union forces have won New Orleans," said Sister Alfred, "and General Lee has invaded Pennsylvania. In France, Emperor Napoleon III is considering the formation of a European alliance to help the Confederacy."

Sister Barbara, who usually remained silent, added, "Though Indiana has been spared as a battleground, we must continue our prayers for peace."

Suddenly a call sounded from the convent yard outside the kitchen. "Sisters! Sisters!" It was Sister Alberta calling as she ran toward the house. The three in the kitchen met her at the door. "Sisters," she cried again, breathlessly. "Father Rachor wants to see us at once. He says he has news of the greatest importance."

"Can the war have ended?" asked Sister Bernard.

"Let us go to the parlor," said Sister Alfred. "We will wait for Father's important news."

Then there was a knocking at the front door, and Sister Alberta went to greet Father Rachor. He came into the parlor looking disturbed, carrying a letter in his hand.

"A letter from the bishop," he said quickly. "I am to inform you of most important instructions which the bishop received from your Motherhouse in France. I wonder if there may be some fear about the safety of Sisters living in a country at war." The priest nervously paced the floor. "Here, I'll read the bishop's letter:

> " 'I have been empowered by Rome to grant these Sisters of Holy Cross their choice of the following three privileges:
>
> 1) To return to the Motherhouse in France
>
> 2) Or to join the society in Canada
>
> 3) Or to enter some other religious society.
>
> " 'Please inform the Sisters in your charge. Very faithfully yours. . . .' "

The priest folded the paper. "The bishop gives no date for your decisions," he said. "I presume this may mean closing our school."

Sister Alfred's eyes were bright. "Undoubtedly the Motherhouse in France has its own view of this war," she said. "I wonder if our future depends upon Napoleon."

The pastor shrugged and went slowly out the door. Sister Alfred turned to Sister Barbara. "Is the excitement too much for you?"

"I feel as Father Rachor must feel—about the school children."

"The letter says we can enter another sisterhood. Perhaps we could do that."

And so it happened. In Chicago, Sister Barbara had heard that the Franciscans from Allegany, New York, would like to establish Franciscan Sisters in the states of Illinois or Indiana.

"Are we sure the Franciscans will accept us?" asked Sister Alberta.

"The Franciscan rule is strict." Sister Barbara spoke up. "Franciscans must trust in God's providence, not talk about it. They are happy serving God."

Sister Alfred offered to write to the Franciscan Fathers at Allegany. "How many of us wish to apply?" she asked.

Sister Barbara.

Sister Alberta.

Sister Bernard.

Sister Alfred.

eleven

MOTHER SUPERIOR

THE four Sisters received their reply from the Franciscan officials. Sister Alfred and her three companions, honorably separated from the Sisters of Holy Cross, would be accepted on trial, they were told.

They were informed that they could stay at Father Rachor's parish in Indiana. A Franciscan priest from Kanakee, Illinois, Father Vanderpool, would be authorized to invest the four sisters as Franciscans.

And as soon as that had been done, the news spread. Father Carl Kuemin requested Franciscan Sisters for his school of St. John the Baptist, in Joliet, Illinois.

Sister Alfred remembered the past. She could hear echoes of a Sister Superior who had said, "If only we were able to do all the things that could be done!"

Around the dining-room table in the convent, the four Sisters discussed their future. Sister Bernard said, "Father Rachor does not want us to leave here. What would become of his school without Sisters?"

"I think," said Sister Alfred, "that we must admit

new candidates. We will need more Sisters as we get other schools."

Very softly Sister Barbara spoke. "I doubt that we have the power to accept others into the sisterhood. That permission must come from Allegany."

"Why do you say so?" the others wanted to know.

"For one thing," replied Sister Barbara, "none of us has yet made vows as a Franciscan."

Even though Sister Barbara did not "faint from excitement" nowadays, or seem so delicate of health as she had been in her younger years, she remained soft-spoken and thoughtful; and everyone listened when Sister Barbara talked.

"We must discuss this with the Franciscan superiors," Sister Barbara continued. "And we should pray for guidance."

One evening after prayers, Sister Alfred made a suggestion. "Two Sisters can stay here in Indiana," she said, "and Sister Bernard and I will go to Father Kuemin's school in Illinois."

That worked out well enough. Sister Alfred and Sister Bernard found the Joliet parish school in the care of Mr. Joseph Wengel from Germany, who had been teaching all the grades by himself.

Again Sister Alfred had a suggestion. Mr. Wengel would continue to teach the boys; the Sisters would teach the girls.

But the situation was far from perfect. The Sisters had no convent in Joliet. They moved into rooms in the upper story of a house near the school. Civil War prices rose higher, till the Sisters were short of money for food. Alarmed, they took in boarding students and started a manufacturing business in their dining room.

They made artificial flowers and bead baskets, embroidered tablecloths, and did fancy sewing which they could sell or trade for provisions. They worked late into the nights, by the light of oil lamps. And when Sister Alfred decided to spend a penny for a newspaper, she read that prices in the Confederate states to the south were much higher than in Illinois—flour three hundred dollars a barrel, boots one hundred fifty dollars a pair, beef six dollars a pound.

In Illinois, Sister Alfred was at least able to trade an embroidered tablecloth for a sack of flour. Some Protestant merchants offered to sell goods to the Sisters at special low prices. They said they wanted to show their appreciation to the Sisters for teaching children of all religions—teaching them mathematics and the sciences and German and French.

In Indiana, Sister Barbara and Sister Alberta did not fare so well, and it became clear that a move had to be made. Sister Alfred wrote to Sister Barbara: "I beg you to tell me if you truly are hungry there. This is a bigger city. There are more people here in Joliet to give us food to eat and to buy our wares." Sister Alfred had reason to fear that Sister Barbara, in her holy way, would hesitate to complain—even perhaps at the risk of her health.

"Another installment of our inheritance is due soon," Sister Alfred wrote. "Let us pray."

After she sealed the letter, Sister Alfred had another thought. Rather than waste postage by ripping the envelope or mailing another, she wrote neatly across the outside:

"Would you buy Federal bonds, or gold pieces, or a house?" The postman who may have read that message on the outside of Sister Alfred's envelope probably didn't know what to think. But Sister Barbara did, and she was resigned to let Sister Alfred make such decisions.

And then the new installment arrived from Luxembourg.

In Joliet, Sister Alfred was thinking hard. The upstairs apartments would be too small for her boarding students if the other Sisters came from Indiana. Perhaps this might be a proper time to use some of her inheritance, to get a house big enough for their needs.

Real-estate prices were still within reason in Joliet, where the townsfolk in their goodness surely made her feel "at home."

So Sister Alfred went looking for a house to buy. She found one near the Hauser place, convenient to the church and school, with two adjoining lots which could be held for future buildings. On March 23, 1864, she paid the owner, Archibald J. McIntyre, six hundred dollars for the house and lots.

She wrote Sister Barbara that the money spent had come from Sister Alfred's own share of the inheritance, since she had not taken the time to get Sister Barbara's approval.

The war seemed to go on forever. In May of 1864, General Grant, in command of all the Federal armies, began his drive toward the Confederate capital of Richmond, Virginia. General Sherman began marching his troops from Chattanooga in Tennessee to Atlanta in Georgia.

Sister Alfred read the newspaper reports of heavy losses in the fighting, and she knew that this must be the struggle to the finish.

Then, in the dark days of the summer, there came a ray of sunshine. The pastor of St. Mary's Church in

Kickapoo, Illinois, needed Sisters for his school—and could assure their financial support. Now all four Sisters could be stationed within the same state. In August, Sister Barbara and Sister Alberta moved from Indiana to Kickapoo, Illinois.

In September, General Sherman took Atlanta and started across Georgia. On December 20, Savannah fell before his onslaught, and he turned northward toward Virginia, to meet Grant's forces, which had laid siege to Petersburg.

By the end of the dreary winter, Sister Alfred's newspaper reading could not keep up with the march of important events. On April 2, Grant took Petersburg. The next day, the Union flag flew over the Confederate capitol at Richmond, and Grant's army, alongside Grant's assistant, General Sheridan, began pursuing the retreating army of the Confederate commander, General Lee. On April 9, Lee surrendered at Appomattox, Virginia. Six days later, President Lincoln was dead—murdered—and the Union victory was shrouded with gloom.

And just then, another ray of sunshine broke the war clouds for Sister Alfred. From Allegany, the Franciscans granted the Illinois Franciscans permission to receive postulants—to accept candidates for the sisterhood. For Sister Alfred, the war, the prices, the poverty, the night work, all the hardships faded in the light of this new hope. She did not even mind that her newspapers now told her of flour that sold for one thousand dollars a barrel in Southern states.

In June of 1865, school was over for the year, and Sister Barbara and Sister Alberta came "home" to Joliet from Kickapoo for the summer. The four Franciscan Sisters, the only four in Illinois, were there the summer day that Mary Ann Rosenberger of Peoria came to them. She was a teacher, too, now on vacation—and she was at long last the candidate they had waited and prayed for: she was applying for admission to the Sisters of Saint Francis!

There was only one thing to do. Sisters Alfred, Bernard, Barbara, and Alberta got on a train with Mary Ann Rosenberger and headed for Allegany, New York. There, on August 2, 1865, Miss Rosenberger was invested with the Franciscan habit and was given the name Sister Mary Angela. On the same day Sister Alfred and her three companions made their first vows as members of the Third Order Regular of the Sisters of Saint Francis—and their perpetual vows as well.

To crown the occasion, Sister Alfred was appointed the first Mother General of the Franciscan Motherhouse in Joliet, Illinois. She protested immediately.

"I should not be the Mother General," she said.

"What's this, Mother Alfred?" Father Pamfilo, the Franciscan Superior, asked her.

"My sister, Sister Barbara, who is older than I—she should be the Mother General."

"I have appointed you, Mother Alfred."

"I beg you to reconsider, Father."

"No." He tried to hide a smile that crept up to the corners of his eyes. "You have the qualities of leadership, Mother Alfred. God gave these to you. This is how it must be."

"Mother Alfred." How strange the words sounded in her ears! But Father Pamfilo's voice, gentle as it was, had been firm and final.

He had chosen her—not her older sister—to be Mother Superior. And deep inside, Mother Alfred felt both humble and pleased.

twelve

THE BUILDER

ON THEIR journey home to Joliet, Mother Alfred and her Franciscan Sisters saw many Union soldiers returning from the war. At the railroad stations and in the trains, they heard soldiers talking.

"What are you going to do when you get home, Sergeant?"

"I'm thinking about railroads. I hear there are plans to lay rails all the way across the continent. How about you?"

"I figure on homesteading."

"That means you'll be moving farther west, doesn't it?"

Mother Alfred could only guess what this would mean to the Franciscan Sisters' future work. If many war veterans were going to claim homesteads, to build new farms and cities, to help lay railroads across the nation, to develop territories into states, it might mean that the sisters, too, would move westward.

Back in Joliet, Mother Alfred began to receive requests from pastors that she send her Sisters to teach in new schools. She promised to do what she could, but most of the young girls who now joined the Franciscan Sisters were not experienced teachers. Mother Alfred had to begin training her candidates before she could agree to staff more schools. She was going to organize a sisterhood of teachers to instruct American children, and she was determined to teach them well.

For the convent in Joliet, she bought a piano, and Sister Barbara began giving piano lessons. Parents thought this a wonderful idea. They too wanted their children to have the best instructions possible—to grow up civilized and "cultured."

As newcomers entered the convent to become Sisters, Mother Alfred personally attended to their training. Those who showed musical ability received piano lessons, and soon there were a number of piano teachers on the staff in Joliet. The Sisters also taught needle art and fancy sewing.

By 1869, Mother Alfred had welcomed seven new Sisters, besides Sister Mary Angela, to Joliet. Now she could send Sister Barbara to fulfill the request from Saint Francis of Assisi School in Chicago, where teachers were needed badly. Because of the emergency, Mother Alfred sent along two novices to help Sister Barbara.

Mother Alfred judged sisters carefully, assigning work to those she was sure were fitted—and willing—for it. And in God's time more and more candidates applied at the Motherhouse, asking to become Sisters.

By 1870, Mother Alfred could count forty Sisters of Saint Francis in eleven schools under her charge—all in Illinois.

By 1875, there were another dozen schools—and from the new schools came new candidates for the sisterhood—from Ohio, Tennessee, Missouri, and Wisconsin, as well as Illinois. As requests for Sisters came from the pastors of new parishes, Mother Alfred sometimes was able to send just two Sisters and a housekeeper to staff a new convent and school; and by the summer of 1876, there were 107 Sisters of Saint Francis teaching in twenty-three schools in five states.

In the meantime Mother Alfred enlarged the Joliet convent, bought more land, and built a convent annex with connecting cloister. The building expenses she paid from "piano lesson receipts" because by this time the Sisters were giving piano lessons to music pupils who came from all around Joliet.

And then, unexpectedly, in 1876 another inheritance installment came from Luxembourg. With Sister Barbara's approval, Mother Alfred sent a letter to the bishop in Chicago, telling him of her hopes for a new Motherhouse. But the bishop had other plans for Mother Alfred. If she were retired as Mother General in Joliet, she would have more time to plan building and expansion elsewhere. And so Mother Alfred was succeeded by Mother Alberta.

In the fall, the Sisters of Saint Francis were asked to

build a new school at Waseca, Minnesota, 400 miles northwest of Joliet. Mother Alfred volunteered to go herself, and, with Mother Alberta's permission, she left for Minnesota to carry out the wishes of the bishop of St. Paul.

Mother Alfred's first impressions of wintry Minnesota remained with her for years. As her train crossed the frozen Mississippi River at Winona, she beheld a river town that reminded her for just a moment of Remich. The frosty hills above the town were hauntingly familiar, but the bustle and busyness of the place assured her that this was new American country.

The icy Mississippi shore was half-jammed with logs, trunks of giant trees from the North Woods. Sawmills on the riverbank, their chimneys spraying soot upon the already gray snow, almost sang out, "Building lumber, building lumber, building. . . ." The train waited just long enough for a woman wearing a heavy coat and wool shawl to board the coach. The newcomer took a seat on the bench across from Mother Alfred and smiled a hello as the train chugged on its way.

"How do you do, Sister? I am Mrs. William Mayo. Are you going to Rochester, by chance?"

"To Waseca," Mother Alfred replied.

"I thought you might be going to Rochester. I have heard that Father O'Gorman has been talking about inviting some Sisters to Rochester to open a school there. This country is growing fast," she added.

"Everything looks very busy," Mother Alfred said.

"My husband says it is the advertising!" Mrs. Mayo smiled again.

"Advertising?"

"The railroads and land companies are telling everybody to come to Minnesota. The posters say that Minnesota's climate is the most invigorating in the world."

"And is it?" Mother Alfred shivered and smiled.

Mrs. Mayo laughed. "All winters are invigorating at thirty below zero. I have managed to survive twenty-two Minnesota winters, though."

Mother Alfred peered thoughtfully out the windows of the train. Perhaps the cold winters and blizzards she had heard about were severe, but she knew that Minnesota farms were rich. In Illinois she had bought flour made from Minnesota wheat. She addressed Mrs. Mayo again, "You say that many people are moving here?"

"My husband says that the advertising is filling Minnesota with sick people and doctors. My husband is a doctor," she added.

"You mean," said Mother Alfred, "sick people are moving to Minnesota for their health?"

"Many are, yes. And, as my husband says," continued Mrs. Mayo, "many doctors follow the sick to Minnesota. You have heard, for example, of towns that have no doctor. But in Rochester—I can name eight doctors whose announcements have been in the newspapers. And several have already moved on to the west and north."

"This is interesting, Mrs. Mayo. Is it possible that Minnesota may become another health resort?"

"Doctor Mayo came here from Indiana in 1854 when he had malaria," replied Mrs. Mayo. "He took his horse and told me he was going to ride out the chills and fever or die. Then, when he was well again, he came back to Indiana and brought our little family to Saint Paul. That year St. Paul had about four thousand people—and thirty doctors. So we moved around Minnesota for nine years before settling in Rochester. The railroads are connecting all these trail towns nowadays."

Mother Alfred looked carefully at Mrs. Mayo. She reflected that sometimes this can happen in life: a sudden mutual understanding and trust between strangers. She nodded when Mrs. Mayo said, "We found Minnesota hard country. My husband is a good doctor, but most of his patients are poor or burdened, and our family fortunes consist of unpaid doctor bills." Mrs. Mayo looked at the floor of the car. "Forgive me, Sister. I should never say these things."

Mother Alfred said slowly, "Your husband must be a good man." She liked Mrs. Mayo. As a Franciscan Sister, Mother Alfred had little social life in the world outside the convent—though Heaven knew that she often had plenty to do in a business way. But instinctively she liked this plainly-dressed woman who had told her in a friendly manner something about the life of a doctor's wife in this frontier state called Minnesota.

Mother Alfred said, "I hope that you had a good visit in Winona, Mrs. Mayo."

"To tell you the truth, I was collecting money as well as visiting people. My husband is in Europe this summer, studying surgery. And we have just bought a farm, with a mortgage. He said I could try to collect overdue bills from his patients while he is away. So I'm trying."

Mother Alfred felt strangely close to this woman.

"I am a money-raiser, too, Mrs. Mayo," she said almost shyly. She glanced self-consciously at the doctor's wife. "I know how hard it is. I will pray for you."

Mrs. Mayo caught Mother Alfred's glance. "I am an Episcopalian." She leaned forward toward the nun. "I will pray for you, too, Sister. I wish you were coming to Rochester."

They fell silent. Portions of her life had been brief friendships like this, Mother Alfred reflected. She claimed no lasting human attachment other than that for her beloved Sister Barbara. Perhaps in Heaven. . . .

At Rochester, Mrs. Mayo said good-by and got off the train, and within minutes the engine and cars rolled on, through snowy fields dotted with frozen creeks and ponds and leafless trees. Then the countryside became rolling plains and little hills with here and there a farm. The snow looked fresh and clean here. In summer, Mother Alfred knew, the chief crop would be wheat. She closed her eyes against the brightness of the fields and did not open them until the train pulled into the station at Owatonna. The newness of the buildings reminded her that Mrs. Mayo had called these "trail towns," now getting new life from the railroads. Mother Alfred grew more anxious than ever to see her destination, Waseca, where the bishop wanted her to start a new school.

She was met at Owatonna by Father Pribyl, pastor of Sacred Heart Parish. "Welcome, Mother Alfred! May I present Mr. Briska?" Mother Alfred nodded to a tall bearded man, who was wearing a buffalo coat and a fur cap.

"We'll go to Waseca in Mr. Briska's sleigh," the priest explained. "You'll stay with the Breen family there."

"You seem to have everything arranged very well, Father," Mother Alfred smiled.

"Certainly," the priest returned her smile. "This is most important. We hear that Rochester also wants Sisters to build new schools. So Waseca must watch out for this competition."

The wagon road was bumpy under the sleigh, but Mr. Briska observed that the weather was warm for a wintry day. To Mother Alfred's questions, he and Father Pribyl replied that this was prosperous wheat country, that the railroads were expected to improve their feeder lines, that the population of the district was growing rapidly. Schools? Schools were needed everywhere, they said.

When they reached Waseca, Mother Alfred declined

to go directly to the Breen family home. "I would rather see the city first," she said.

It was a small town, smaller than she had expected to find. "The population is greater than you might think," Mr. Briska told her. "Most of our people live on farms. The children will come into the city to attend school, just as most of the people do now for church. Our church is downtown near the courthouse."

"The school, our new academy, probably should be elsewhere," Mother Alfred said. "May we drive around the city?"

Her companions listened closely to her remarks about city planning. "A courthouse," she told them, "will determine the locations of the main shops and businesses. Your lake here in town will influence the growth of the city's best neighborhoods."

"And what of churches?" asked Father Pribyl.

"I have watched this in other cities," Mother Alfred said. "Usually houses are built first, and then the churches are placed amidst the houses. But of course it would be better to plan ahead, to plan the churches and the schools. Then the houses would follow."

Mr. Briska nodded. "I wish we could do that," he told Mother Alfred. "But a town like this just springs up where the wagon trails come together to make a marketplace for the settlers. Now the new railroad is bringing more trade and more people, and the town is growing rapidly. Perhaps we can some day plan ahead, as you say, Mother Alfred."

" 'Some day' may never come," she said firmly. "Let us ride out of town toward the other lakes you mentioned in your letter, Father. I would like to see the sights beyond the city boundaries."

Mr. Briska slackened his reins and the horse stepped faster. "It is fair enough weather for a drive," he chuckled, "but is it possible you wish to buy a farm in our wilderness?"

"The city of Minneapolis is growing around its lakes," said Father Pribyl.

"Milling and railroads cause such growth," Mr. Briska broke in. "Minneapolis will take milling business from these little towns. The men who control the railroads can build a city or ruin it. I have heard the campaign speeches by Doctor Mayo, who calls the railroad owners and the wheat buyers *robbers* and *plunderers!*"

"Doctor Mayo?" Mother Alfred asked in surprise. "From Rochester?"

"You have heard of him?" Mr. Briska seemed surprised.

"Just today," Mother Alfred replied. "Is he a politician? I gathered that he is a friend of those in need."

"He is well known for his generosity," Mr. Briska agreed.

"He was well known as a doctor before he entered politics," Father Pribyl broke in. "Perhaps a farmer or a tradesman would be less quick to call other men robbers and plunderers."

"Doctor Mayo is a friend of farmers," the bearded

man insisted. "I remember the years that our wheat prices were forced down to forty cents and our freight rates were raised. I am still in debt—even for this horse."

They fell silent again, and the mortgaged horse trudged along over the snow, slipping now and again as the driver urged him to a trot.

The driver turned toward Mother Alfred and said, "There is Clear Lake, to the left." He pointed to a hilly point overlooking a bowl-like expanse of frozen water, decorated along the edges with clumps of dark trees.

"Beautiful," whispered Mother Alfred. "What a lovely spot for an academy!" The two men looked at her in surprise.

"I'm not sure," Father Pribyl muttered, "that this is what the people had in mind when they decided on a school."

"The situation is perfect for a country boarding school," Mother Alfred said. "The environment is much better here than downtown where the roughnecks are."

"It is a fine idea," Mr. Briska said. "But I think Father Pribyl will agree that there are some Catholics here in Waseca who may have to be convinced of it first."

"I will not quarrel," Mother Alfred said, "but my instructions make it clear that our Motherhouse will bear the expense and therefore the responsibility for selecting a site."

"Please, Mother Alfred, do not be too hard on my parishioners," Father Pribyl smiled. "We have not really asked them about this site yet."

"Of course, Father. I spoke hastily."

"Mr. Briska," Father Pribyl asked brightly, "do you know who owns this property? I think we should help Mother Alfred buy it immediately."

The lakeside property was purchased, but the Waseca academy was never built. The people who wanted the Sisters of Saint Francis to build them a school did not want it where Mother Alfred said it should be—away from downtown. She thought that they would change their minds, and meanwhile parishioners in nearby Owatonna agreed to Father Pribyl's suggestion that an academy be built in their town.

She bought land in Owatonna—not out in the country—in March, 1877, and awarded contracts for a three-story building to house a day school and a private school for children of all faiths.

Two months later, Mother Alfred received a surprise visit from Rochester's Father O'Gorman, of whom she had heard almost as much as she had of Doctor Mayo. Father O'Gorman assured Mother Alfred that his people not only wanted a school—they wanted, as well, to pay for the land themselves. He promised to buy a block of land for an academy in Rochester.

Mother Alfred accepted Father O'Gorman's invitation to build a school in Rochester. She hired contractors to begin building that June. And she went back to Joliet to get more Sisters and as much furniture as Mother Alberta could spare for the new schools in Minnesota.

That fall, Mother Alfred had new academies in two Minnesota towns. There were sixty pupils in Owatonna and 210 in Rochester. Her work made headlines in a number of newspapers, and in Chicago Bishop Foley became concerned about the sudden demand for Sisters in faraway Minnesota—a demand greater than the supply in Illinois.

The bishop could see that Mother Alfred was, as usual, working faster than any other Sister he knew about—perhaps too fast for the calm and orderliness of the sisterhood in Joliet. He decided to establish Mother Alfred in a brand new Motherhouse, with Sister Barbara and as many other Sisters as wished to join the new group.

Twenty-four Sisters followed Mother Alfred to Minnesota, and on December 23, 1877, Mother Alfred found herself a Mother General again, this time in charge of twenty-four Sisters, two academies in Minnesota, and St. Mary's School in Portsmouth, Ohio, where the pastor, Father Noonan, chose to put his schools under Mother Alfred's new sisterhood.

In the Minnesota academies, enrollments grew, assuring Mother Alfred that many people wanted their children to be educated by the Sisters. Often parents brought their boys and girls—Protestants as well as Catholics—to Mother Alfred to study German and French and music.

Mother Alfred journeyed to St. Paul, where the bishop approved the new Franciscan foundation at Rochester and told her to build her novitiate by seeking new recruits from the Sisters' schools. Among the first to come was Mary Dempsey of Rochester, who became Sister Joseph on August 6, 1878.

Soon Mother Alfred opened schools at five more towns in Minnesota and another dozen in Ohio and Kentucky.

In Rochester, where the parishioners had pledged to buy the land, notes fell due and could not be paid. Mother Alfred dipped into her treasury, where she had placed past inheritance installments, and paid the notes. To the amazed pastor, she explained, "We stretch money by buying in proper season, making it do double duty and sometimes more. Your parishioners cannot pay their notes now because business is bad and many of them are suffering. Let us hire the unemployed and turn these hardships to our advantage. This would be a good time to complete our buildings at reasonable cost."

With the help of inheritance money, all of these projects were paid for.

thirteen

THE HOSPITAL

A STREAK of sunlight filtered through a dusty window of the old barn where Mother Alfred had been sitting, musing, remembering.

"How long have I been resting here, thinking of the past?" she wondered. "I must get back. The rain has stopped."

She stepped out of the barn. The air smelled clean as she walked through the farmyard, glancing toward the windows of the house as she drew close to the steps. At the doorway she saw a woman watching, and Mother Alfred waved and said hello.

"I spent the rainstorm in your barn."

"I saw you." The woman sighed: "My husband went to town to get me some headache powders!"

"Have you had a doctor?"

"No, but I will have to go to one if I don't feel better soon."

"Thanks for the shelter." Mother Alfred nodded toward the barn. "Tell me, could I send a doctor to you?"

"No, thank you," the woman replied.

Mother Alfred waved a good-by and went on down the yard to the road.

She thought again about building a hospital in Rochester. She would have to raise money. What had Doctor Mayo said—forty-thousand dollars?

Of course, she had never built a hospital. Her Sisters were teachers and not nurses, as she had told Bishop John Ireland of Saint Paul when he had suggested a hospital, months ago. She decided that she would have to move slowly, one step at a time, choosing her workers carefully.

She would have to handle this in her own way.

Mother Alfred walked toward the convent, her idea now resting lightly in the back of her mind.

At the back door of the convent, Sister Mary Martha was sweeping.

"Oh, hello, Mother Alfred. Did you check the garden after the rain?" The big jolly sister nodded her head toward the garden plot at the back of the convent block.

"No, Sister, I must confess that I did not. I guess I was thinking too hard about something else."

Then Mother Alfred went into the convent and back on duty, calm and confident again.

And then, one day Doctor William Mayo, the elder, came to the convent, carrying a role of papers under his arm.

"Mother Superior, I suppose you thought I had forgotten. Perhaps I was waiting for one of your Sisters to be sick, Heaven forbid. I do talk a bit wildly sometimes, don't I, Mother Superior?"

"You seem to be in a good mood today, Doctor. Come into the dining room, will you please?"

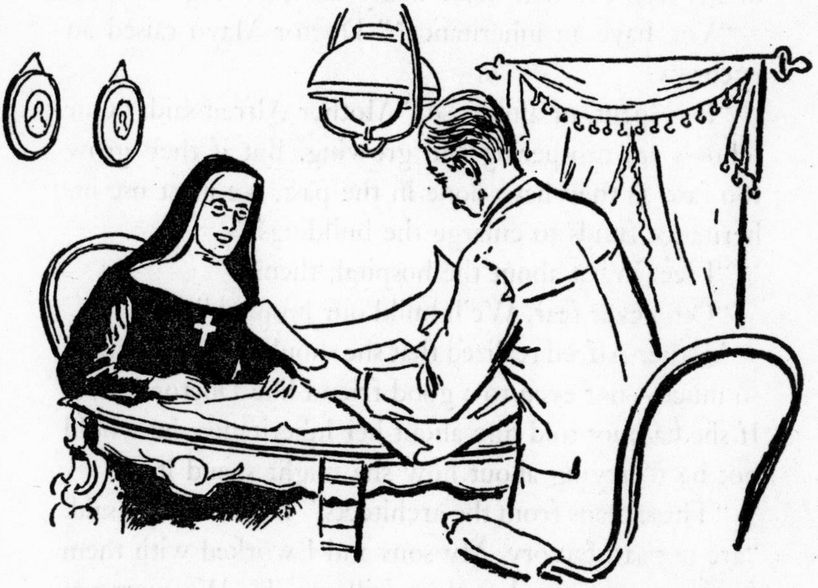

Mother Alfred's "office" in the convent was the dining room; it reminded her of home in Remich, and of her father. Mother Alfred knew that most Americans favored a room called an "office" for business affairs, and she had an office at the academy and in her schools across the country. But here at home in the convent, she used the dining room more often than her study.

"At home we use our family dining room for consultations, too," Doctor Mayo smiled.

"I am not sentimental, Doctor, but dining rooms remind me of our family home in Remich. We discussed many things in our dining room—business matters, too. It was there that we first learned of our inheritance and of the iron ore that made many Luxembourgers rich."

"You have an inheritance?" Doctor Mayo raised an eyebrow.

"It is spent, or almost so," Mother Alfred said. "Our schools are prospering and growing. But if they grow too fast, as they have done in the past, we must use inheritance funds to enlarge the buildings."

"I see. What about the hospital, then?"

"Oh, never fear. We'll build our hospital."

Mother Alfred realized that she should not have talked so much—not even to a good friend like Doctor Mayo. If she had not told him about her inheritance, he would not be worrying about how she might spend it.

"These plans from the architects," Doctor Mayo said, "are not satisfactory. My sons and I worked with them for many months, but they will not do. We must get these exactly right."

"I agree, Doctor Mayo."

"I wish to take as much time as possible for these plans. My sons and I should go East again, perhaps to Europe, maybe next year. Mother Superior, don't you agree that we should take time to get the plans right?"

"As you say, Doctor. You are the chief of staff."

"All right, then. I'll send the plans back twice and thrice if necessary, until we get them as we want."

Mother Alfred was watching the convent bills more closely these days than she had done in some years. She was setting aside dollars every month—building the treasury of the Sisters of Saint Francis, quietly, efficiently, steadily.

The money-raising went along uneventfully until Bishop Purcell of Ohio sent a letter:

"Dear Mother General—

"As you know, the Third Plenary Council of Baltimore has stressed the need for excellence in schools taught by Catholic Sisters. To safeguard the standards of schools in this diocese, teaching sisters will now take examinations under my direction. Very faithfully yours—"

Mother Alfred tapped the bishop's envelope against the table and studied the letter again. She had many schools in Ohio now—in Cincinnati, Cleveland, Toledo, Portsmouth, Ripley, Woodsfield, Ironton. Some of her Sisters were very young, and many were teaching children in the early grades while continuing their own education.

It was possible that some of her Sisters might fail His Excellency's examination. Then what would happen? If they could not pass the test to teach, and if other bishops were to give tests, some might have to be dismissed from Mother Alfred's Franciscan sisterhood.

A thought came to her that had popped into her mind before, a little joke which she told herself sometimes while she dreamed and made her building plans. "If only my hardworking Sisters were bricklayers," she began, smiling to herself. Mother Alfred straightened in her chair. "I know!" she cried. "Anyone who fails the bishop's tests for teachers could mop floors and do ward work in our hospital while continuing her studies."

Mother Alfred issued new orders to the Sisters at her twenty schools in Minnesota, Ohio, Kentucky, and Missouri. They were to try to save every cent possible and to send it to the Motherhouse at Rochester for building funds. When possible they would accept gifts of food and clothing in order to save money, would take in extra work for pay and would send the proceeds to Rochester. Where the Sisters had a piano, they would seek music pupils. They would sell needlework and fancy sewing. In Rochester, Mother Alfred opened "pre-school" classes for children between three and six. Every dollar counted.

Through these years, the Sisters wore cheap shoes and rough cloth garments—and mended and re-mended them. They ate soup instead of meat for some meals, and their diet was planned for health rather than luxury. To save money, they made their own soap, did their own manual labor such as firing the furnaces and chopping wood. They made and sold wax flowers. Several talented Sisters painted pictures, and other Sisters sold them.

The Sisters knew that they were sacrificing for new buildings. But Bishop Ireland had not authorized an announcement about a hospital. Everyone seemed to agree that a new building would be needed for the crowded Academy of Our Lady of Lourdes right there in Rochester.

Every time Doctor Mayo came to the convent, sometimes with his son Will, Mother Alfred wondered why no other Sister guessed what the visits might be about. Still, who but Bishop Ireland and Mother Alfred would so much as dream about a hospital in Rochester in the 1880's? After all, the idea had frightened Doctor Mayo. Who else could possibly guess such a thing?

Doctor Mayo and Doctor Will sat in the dining room with Mother Alfred and talked about hospital plans. They had ideas for ventilating systems, for a surgery room with a slanting floor that could be flooded with water that would drain off into a pipe, for a boiler on the kitchen stove to pipe hot water upstairs. And they decided again that they would visit Eastern hospitals to study more. But there was still no hurry; Mother Alfred was very patient.

By 1887, she was ready to announce her surprise. She had money enough for a hospital as well as for other buildings. It was all here in the treasury, in dollars and cents. And then one day she called together the Sisters in the "corporation," the older nuns named to this governing board by the Bishop, and told them of her plan. She gave three reasons for wanting to build a hospital:

1) A hospital provides works of mercy, to serve God in His suffering creatures;

2) A hospital would help the Sisters accept and keep more girls with vocations to serve God as nurses;
3) Bishop Ireland had suggested a hospital several years ago.

Mother Alfred watched the faces of the Sisters in the room. She noticed a half dozen nodding in silent approval of the idea. Others seemed to be smiling, which could mean that they liked the plan or thought it foolish. Well, all they had to do was vote and get it over with.

Outdoors, the sun suddenly stopped shining. In the distance, thunder rumbled across the countryside. Then lightning pierced the grayness of the sky. The Sisters, one and all, turned to look out the windows. In other parts of town, they knew, people would be hurrying to the storm cellars that almost everyone had built since the tornado of 1883. Slowly, one by one, the Sisters turned to watch Mother Alfred. Would she order them to run for the basement?

"No tornado this time," Mother Alfred said calmly. "Just a thunderstorm. But if the winds should get stronger, we might all go to the basement—just to be sure."

From the back row the small voice of Sister Barbara could be heard. "I move," she said softly, "that we vote on the question of building a new hospital."

The sisters voted—forty-eight to five—to build a new hospital. Mother Alfred was satisfied. She personally considered the hospital one of the best ideas of her long life.

Bishop Ireland gave his approval to the project on August 29, 1887. Sister Gabriel cheered the news. She told Mopsy, the Saint Bernard dog, "Maybe Mother Alfred will let you eat meat again, instead of soup bones." Still, Mopsy was luckier than Oppy, who was Mother Alfred's pet possum until he started to eat too expensively. After Oppy stole sugar, he was set free in the wooded fields west of the convent to find his own food. Mopsy could be grateful; he had been kept on the staff during the "lean times."

The next month, Mother Alfred asked Doctor Mayo to go with her to a farm owned by John Ostrum west of the city limits. Mr. Ostrum was willing to sell nine acres of his land for two thousand dollars. Remembering her Waseca plans for a building outside town, Mother Alfred wanted to get Doctor Mayo's ideas about her choice of a location.

"Excellent," said Doctor Mayo. "The quiet and the country air should be ideal for hospital patients."

"Rochester will grow, Doctor Mayo, and so will this hospital. Later on we can keep our neighborhood quiet by buying large grounds around it."

"I agree, Mother Superior. I think you should buy this property."

When Doctor Mayo next came to Saint Francis' Convent for a dining room conference, young Doctor Will and Charlie—now Doctor Charlie—came with him. The plans were almost ready now; trips to New York and other cities of the East had been worth while.

A few more improvements, and the final plans would be ready.

Old Doctor Mayo once said, in the dining room, "This hospital will be a great experiment." Young Will, as usual, looked serious and said nothing.

But young Doctor Charlie smiled broadly at Mother Alfred. "We'll get lots of patients from all these towns around here," Charlie said. "Mother Alfred, I think this is a great idea."

Mother Alfred was pleased to hear Doctor Charlie talk this way, but she could see that neither young Doctor Will nor his father shared Charlie's optimism. "Besides ourselves, I have been unable to obtain a single doctor for the staff," the old doctor told Mother Alfred. "Everyone has politely refused."

"Why is this, Doctor?"

"Nobody will say. I suppose some think the hospital is doomed. And I think there is some anti-Catholic feeling behind this."

"The cause of suffering humanity knows no religion; the charity of the Sisters of Saint Francis is as broad as their religion," Mother Alfred said.

Old Doctor Mayo nodded. "I agree with you, Mother Superior. But I think we should be willing to expect some rough sledding, perhaps."

And if some Sister, worn and weary, might have heard old Doctor Mayo talk about "rough sledding," she might have laughed. Little did he know of the labors and the scrimping on food and clothing that had made it possible for Mother Alfred to build a hospital for the use of the surrounding country.

On one Ohio trip that summer, Mother Alfred rode a riverboat because the fare was fifty cents cheaper than the train. The boat was slower, but she merely charged the "lost time" against hours of sleep that she contributed to her building fund. At her mission schools and chapels she showed the Sisters how to polish candlesticks with soft stones, as metalworkers had done for centuries in Luxembourg. The Sisters used floursacks for pillowcases, to save the price of "store-bought" goods.

Nowadays when Mother Alfred came home from downtown or from her necessary travels, she did not bring presents for her Sisters the way she used to do. Everyone knew that Mother Alfred was saving money for the building fund, saving still, and here it was spring in 1888.

Rochester's Academy of Our Lady of Lourdes was more crowded than ever. There was money in the treasury for building, but Mother Alfred was waiting for the "proper season" to add classrooms. And when that season arrived, it came with a bang—two contractors bid prices that were "too good to turn down" on the two buildings. And within three months she had both her hospital and her academy addition under way, a mile apart.

Mother Alfred ordered three new stories for the

academy, to double its size. Off came the roof, up went three new floors.

Her timing was good; the hospital bid was half the forty thousand dollars that Doctor Mayo had estimated five years before; and she had doubled the size of the academy for eleven thousand more. Furthermore, the hospital contract had almost another year to run. If necessary, the treasury could be replenished again.

In the fall she sent Bishop Ireland an invitation to bless the academy addition. He came to Rochester from Saint Paul for the ceremony. He wanted, too, to investigate the progress on the hospital building. "When will it be ready, Mother Alfred?"

"Our contract says next summer, Your Excellency."

"Who will manage the hospital?"

"I have selected a Sister."

"What about yourself?" the bishop asked.

"I am a teacher, and a money-raiser."

"I suggest that you think about taking charge of the hospital yourself, Mother Alfred."

"I do not understand, Your Excellency."

"We wish to avoid all trouble," he said. "You can get along with people—all kinds of people." The bishop took a deep breath. Was it possible that the Mother Superior had not heard the rumors, the gossip, that had reached his chancery office?

He looked at Mother Alfred's face. It was a simple face, honest, sincere, and not so tense and worried now as he had seen it before when her money worries were greater. Now this remarkable face showed just a trace of wonder because the bishop had hinted that something might be wrong about the hospital.

Yes, it was possible that she did not know of the gloomy talk. In the first place, trouble-makers would not come to Mother Alfred. She was too busy to be bothered with nonsense or gossip, or to be discouraged by gloomy people.

She did not know that some Catholics in Rochester had complained about her to the bishop. They said it was wrong for Mother Alfred to build a hospital for the Mayo doctors, who were not Catholics. They wanted the bishop to assign Catholic doctors to the hospital.

The bishop spoke again. "There is bad feeling," he said, "among some of the Catholic lay people. In their way of thinking, a non-believer will be the physician-in-charge of your Catholic hospital. Do you understand?"

"What is a Catholic hospital, after all?" Mother Alfred wondered aloud. "We will call this 'Saint Mary's Hospital' and we plan a chapel and a cross for the building. But none of the diseases or illnesses will be 'Catholic.' Is this not ridiculous, Your Grace?"

"Of course, of course," he replied. "But because there might be trouble over Doctor Mayo's political activities, it may be necessary to put you in charge of the hospital when it is ready, Mother Alfred. For now, God bless you."

After the bishop had gone back to St. Paul Mother

Alfred wondered what he had been trying to say to her. "For now, God bless you." Doctor Mayo is a Democrat, but my bankers are Republicans, she thought. What foolish troubles people make for themselves!

In November, work on the hospital building moved into a race against winter. Bricks and mortar are not easy to work with in cold Minnesota winters. Plaster may freeze, metals shrink, other materials break like icicles.

Work was slow because the men had to stop to put up canvas windbreakers for the rusty stoves that melted ice into water for mortar and plaster. Sometimes they had to dig their equipment out of snowdrifts; some mornings they spent chipping ice from their scaffolding. But they raced the summer deadline of their contractor's bond, losing time with each cold day until, with the building half finished, the contractor left Minnesota by train in the middle of the night.

Mother Alfred's friends in the city and on the railroad told her of the contractor's flight, but she was able to protect herself. Two bondsmen who had guaranteed the building came to her aid, and the building was finished on time and for the amount she had agreed to pay.

She had plenty to think about—between finances and worrying about the bishop's intentions for her and the hospital. She asked Doctor Mayo what he knew of Catholic opposition to their plans.

"None," he replied, "but I know some folks who don't like nuns and popes."

"Apparently the bishop has heard of both kinds of bigotry."

"Are you surprised, Mother Superior?" Doctor Mayo shook his head and wondered how a Sister who knew so much about many things could know so little about other matters. "Anyway, Mother Superior, it cannot be jealousy that is troubling our critics. Who in the world would be jealous of a doomed hospital—or of an old doctor?"

"The bishop says I may have to be in charge of the hospital."

"Good!" cried Doctor Mayo. "With you in charge, I may be able to develop a workable plan for the hospital."

That plan was Mrs. Mayo's, he admitted. She had suggested that they have their friend John Willis Baer, a Presbyterian gentleman of good reputation throughout Olmsted County, accept an appointment as special superintendent of Saint Mary's Hospital. Mother Alfred agreed, and jolly Mr. Baer went around town proudly telling everyone of his fine hospital, which, he said, would be open to patients of any faith or none.

In mid-July the bishop came again, this time to present the Franciscan habit to eight new girls who wanted to become Sisters. The Motherhouse would be able to accept new schools next term.

The bishop had something else on his mind. He assembled the Sisters in the chapel that evening and announced an immediate election to select a new Mother General. Mother Alfred, he explained, would not be a candidate for re-election.

There it was.

Like a tornado.

You know that tornados can happen, of course. You have that much warning. And the bishop had said last year that a change might be necessary.

From across the convent yard, from far across Minnesota and the Mississippi River and the prairies of Wisconsin and Illinois and Indiana, Mother Alfred could almost hear echoes of long ago.

"All you have to do is to be obedient."

She would have to vote with the Sisters. She turned in a blank ballot, because she could not think clearly at the moment. The Sisters balloted twice. Something seemed to be wrong. The Sisters were unable to choose a new Mother General. Perhaps they could not think clearly, either. This election was unexpected. Then the bishop spoke again. The regulations which he had revised for Mother Alfred last year would permit him to appoint a Sister of his own choice to be the new Mother General.

His choice was Sister Matilda.

Sister Matilda, said the bishop, will become Mother Matilda, in full charge of the Sisters in the Midwestern states, in charge of the Motherhouse and the academies and the schools and—actually in charge of the new hospital. Although Mother Alfred could be assigned to direct the hospital, everything would be under the authority of Mother Matilda.

This was not the way Mother Alfred might have arranged matters. Nor so soon. But the bishop had spoken. She resigned herself to his decisions.

Mother Alfred thought about the new young Mother Matilda. She had come to the Motherhouse in Joliet twenty years before—a girl of eighteen, Katie Wagner, daughter of immigrants from Prussia. Six years later her sister Christina entered the sisterhood—there she was now, Sister Euphemia. Both had come from Illinois to Minnesota with Mother Alfred. The new Mother General was only half Mother Alfred's age.

There was more excitement among the Sisters now, for they were to choose a First Assistant to the new Mother General. The Sisters voted, the ballots were counted and—the First Assistant was Mother Alfred!

The position, like the title "Mother" from now on, would be an honor. She would help the new Mother General get acquainted with her duties; and she would still be called "Mother," but just for old times' sake.

Near the door, Sister Barbara waited. "How are you, Sister?" She might have called her *Marie* again, but "Sister" would do from a real-life sister.

"Well enough," replied Mother Alfred. "The bishop warned me about this last year."

"God's will be done," said Sister Barbara.

"Amen."

Young Mother Matilda tiptoed to Mother Alfred's side. "I will welcome your help as my First Assistant, and I hope that you will tell me what I can do in return."

Mother Alfred's eyes grew bright. "I have one request immediately," she told the new young Mother General. "Sister Joseph is teaching at Ashland, Kentucky. She should be transferred to our hospital. I have intended this since the night of that terrible tornado years ago. Sister Joseph, it seems to me, was born to be a nurse."

"It shall be arranged, Mother Alfred, as soon as possible."

Now Mother Alfred could give her full attention to Saint Mary's Hospital. The townsfolk and the newspapers already had discovered its impressiveness, a great building of red brick and white stone, rising above a stone basement to a height of more than three stories, with a large cross at the top. The windows were shuttered, there were four fancy balconies on the upper stories, and there were curtains in the bedrooms to make Saint Mary's Hospital as "homelike" as possible.

Old Doctor Mayo and Mother Alfred toured the building many times that fall of 1889, planning the "formal opening" for October 1.

In the basement, the old doctor explained to her the dispensary rooms, the laundry's handiness to the cistern for five hundred gallons of water which the sisters could pump by hand for use in the hospital, and the "foul air room" from which his ventilating system would blow out the hospital odors.

"Over here, Mother Superior, in this shaft all the way up to the top of the hospital, we'll have an elevator car. My son, Doctor Charles, will build us an elevator."

"He can do many things, can he not, Doctor Mayo?"

"He has mechanical genius. As a boy he rigged a steam engine to run the pump on our well at home. He hooked up a telephone from our farm house to my offices downtown. And he'll make other improvements here at the hospital."

The first floor had offices for all three of the doctors, and reception parlors, dining rooms, and a kitchen.

On the second floor, in the women's wards and private rooms decorated to look "like home," the Sisters had spread gay coverlets on the beds. And on this floor, Doctor Mayo's operating room with the slanting and self-draining floor was built out from the north wall, so that the operating table stood under a skylight in the ceiling.

"Charles built that operating table," the old doctor said. "He designed it to take advantage of this specially skylighted room. Most doctors agree that 'north light' is the best possible medical light for surgery."

The third floor, for men, had a recreation room where patients could read or walk around and visit with each other. Here also was the chapel, though there was at present no chance of having a chaplain. There were not even enough priests in Southern Minnesota in 1889 to take care of the parishes.

Doctor Mayo counted the beds on these rounds

through the empty hospital. "Twenty-seven regular beds," he would say, "and eighteen emergency beds ready."

"Are you worrying about filling them, Doctor?" Mother Alfred asked.

"Well, not exactly. I was thinking that a forty-five bed hospital, or even a twenty-seven bed hospital, would be a fair building for a city the size of Chicago. And here we are in the country, a mile west of a town of five thousand souls, waiting to see what will happen! Mother Alfred, you do amaze me!"

fourteen

END OF THE ROAD

AND NOW that their hospital was finished, how would they "open" it?

Have a tornado?

An epidemic?

Advertise for sick customers?

No. Doctors order some patients to go to hospitals, because doctors usually can work best in hospitals. That was how Saint Mary's Hospital must begin, Mother Alfred knew.

There would be new ideas for people to get used to, Doctor Mayo explained one day to Mother Alfred when they were talking in the new building. Some day, he said, patients would come to the hospital for "observation." But people were not ready for that idea yet. And there was another new idea, very important. People would have to get used to paying "hospital bills" as well as doctor bills—which, Doctor Mayo could tell the world, were slow enough.

"I have another idea, which your older son, Doctor Will, does not approve of," Mother Alfred told the old Doctor. "I think it would be wise to have a special school to teach nurses."

"Will says he doesn't like that idea?"

"He told me that nurses must be 'born' to the profession. I agree that some people seem to have special talents, of course. But I believe that these talents must be trained —and that some skills can be taught to less-gifted persons. So I would plan a school of nursing some day."

"You are looking ahead, Mother Superior."

"I have arranged for Sister Joseph to be transferred here soon."

"Wonderful. She could make a great career in medicine."

"I have picked a number of others for hospital work, too."

"And Mrs. Mayo and I," the old doctor chuckled, "selected John Baer for our superintendent. We have a staff now, but we will not get many patients until we get more doctors to come here. So far, not one doctor will risk sending a patient here."

Mother Alfred once more reassured the old doctor. "Doctor Will and Doctor Charlie have been telling me about the boiled water and carbolic acid and other fluids used nowadays in the new antiseptic surgery. Doctor Mayo, these boys are far ahead of other doctors. I have every confidence that our hospital will be a great success."

The old doctor wheeled around where he stood. "Was that thunder I heard?"

Winds whistled outside, where the sky was darkening. Then more thunder and lightning crackled in the distance.

"A storm is brewing, Mother Superior! Another tornado, do you suppose?"

"Not a tornado—but a windstorm. It could blow away our hay in the hospital yard." Mother Alfred headed for the stairway. "I wonder if we could get it in before the storm hits here."

"Hay?" Doctor Mayo shrugged. "I have hay in the fields at home, too. There will be more hay another season."

She ran full speed, three or four Sisters following her—and these trailed by the doctor, his frock coattails flying behind him in the wind.

Across the field, Mother Alfred and her nuns pulled a farm wagon, tugging it by the tongue as if they were a team of horses. They got the load covered and safe beside the back wall of the new brick building before the first big drops of rain began to fall. The winds died down, and the Sisters returned to their work inside the hospital.

Doctor Mayo followed Mother Alfred along a corridor. "Mother Superior, how much is that hay worth?"

"I don't know the market price, Doctor, but it is

worth more by far now than if a windstorm had blown it away."

As it turned out, Saint Mary's Hospital never had a formal opening with pomp and ceremony, after all.

On September 30, 1889, the Mayos had an emergency operation to perform on a patient with a cancerous eye. Doctor Charlie did the surgery, Doctor Will was assistant surgeon, and their father was the anesthetist. Saint Mary's Hospital was a reality, at last. Within a week, eight patients had been admitted.

Mother Alfred may not have known it, but her unendowed hospital was one of the first to accept patients who could not pay for their care. Saint Mary's was open to all sick persons, whatever their finances, their color, or their religion. Those who could pay were charged one dollar a day for a bed in a ward, or six dollars a week—and eight dollars a week for a private room. Both Saint Mary's and the Mayos began a "no-money—no-payment" policy that is still working.

When the school year started that fall of 1889, Mother Alfred helped Mother Matilda at the Motherhouse, while Sister Hyacinth was in charge of the new hospital. The Mayos told their patients to pay the Sisters' bill first—before paying the doctor's bill. At the end of the first month, Sister Hyacinth had received almost one hundred dollars in payments. With this money she bought food for more than twenty patients and for seven Sisters, bought kerosene for the lanterns that the nurses carried on their night rounds, paid for the city water that was piped into the cistern in the hospital basement, and ordered coal for the furnace.

Those were the only expenses on Saint Mary's books when Mother Alfred took over as hospital superior the following month, November of 1889. She decided that some money could be spared for making the rooms more attractive. Counting pennies, Mother Alfred bought oilcloth and pinked it herself to make covers for the washstands in the rooms. As the cold closed in on Minnesota that November, Mother Alfred bought several new blankets for patients' beds—and watched the coal bill closely. She supervised the furnace-room herself, shoveling coal and banking the fire as economically as possible . . . and teaching the other Sisters how to do it properly.

Meanwhile, upstairs, a newcomer to Saint Mary's was teaching hospital nursing to seven Sisters. She was Miss Edith Graham of Rochester, who had studied nursing in Chicago and was now the Mayos' medical assistant—and was also Doctor Charlie's fiancée. Her appointment at Saint Mary's was temporary. She would stay just long enough for the Sisters to learn the work. And her star pupil was Sister Joseph, who had at last arrived from Kentucky.

Late that month, Pope Leo XIII created a new diocese in Minnesota, with the Cathedral to be at Winona. This meant that Rochester and the Sisters of Saint

Francis and Saint Mary's Hospital would now be under a new bishop, the Most Reverend Joseph B. Cotter.

Bishop Cotter was known in Southern Minnesota as a diplomat; and when he gave his approval to Saint Mary's Hospital, Mother Alfred could breathe more easily. Three Masonic lodges in Rochester paid one hundred fifty dollars for a bed at Saint Mary's—against the time that some of their members might be sick. The County Commissioners appropriated public money to pay for care to the needy, and Protestant friends of Saint Mary's raised money for the hospital by holding a public ball.

As more patients came to Saint Mary's, the hospital needed more Sisters. When, that winter, the staff numbered eleven, Mother Matilda could spare no more Sisters to become student nurses.

Mother Alfred had to show the way. Sometimes she worked continuous shifts of one day, a night, and another day. She carried water from the basement reservoir to the second and third floors of the hospital, carried trays of food from the kitchen to the same floors. The Sisters walked into town each day to do their marketing after supper, and carried the purchases home in their arms. They had no carriages.

Doctor Charlie had not yet installed his telephone system; the Sisters had to walk to the Mayo offices in town or out to the family farm if a doctor were needed in an emergency.

The hospital linens were laundered and ironed after

supper each evening. The housekeeping in the rooms was done before the Sisters' bedtime—usually about midnight. And the Sisters' day began about four o'clock in the morning—unless they had been up all night with sick patients.

Mother Alfred and her Sister-nurses were struggling harder now than ever before in their lives—twenty hours a day, seven days each week. Their chapel on the third floor of the hospital stood empty; the Bishop could spare no chaplain for them. On Sunday mornings, the Sisters often had to miss Mass because there were patients too sick to leave for the time it took to walk a mile into town, spend an hour in church, and walk back again. As for daily Mass, that was out of the question.

Three months after the opening of Saint Mary's, sixty-two patients had been admitted, treated or operated upon, and returned home. Receipts were more than three hundred dollars. The hospital treasury could pay its bills. Mother Alfred now approved an idea of Sister Hyacinth, to hire girls to work as hospital maids and to pay them out of hospital earnings.

Saint Mary's was supporting itself.

In February, Mother Alfred took a vacation trip to see Sister Barbara, who was now in charge of Sacred Heart Institute in Ironton, Ohio. She placed Sister Augustine in charge and went to say good-by to Doctor Mayo. He suggested that they talk in the hospital dining room.

"You are becoming sentimental, Doctor?"

"Why not, Mother Superior? Saint Mary's Hospital is proving itself a marvelous success, just as you told me it would."

"It is God's will, Doctor Mayo. Without Him we can do nothing."

"You are working very hard, Mother Superior. And so are all the Sisters on the hospital staff."

"Perhaps. But I don't think that we work any harder than the doctors. You have hours similar to our own—and more responsibility."

"I think that we get more sleep, Mother Superior. And your responsibility is very great, caring for these lives that we doctors leave in your hands and your care."

"The ways of the Lord are unsearchable," Mother Alfred said quietly. "My father the blacksmith used to say that in his dining room at home in Remich. The ways of the Lord are unsearchable."

"Have a good vacation, Mother Superior. You have earned it. Please give my best to Sister Barbara."

"And please give mine to Mrs. Mayo," Mother Alfred said.

Mother Alfred did not return to Rochester for two months. When Doctor Mayo asked how she found Sister Barbara, Mother Alfred replied that her sister was well. Doctor Mayo could only guess that Mother Alfred had been ill herself—or she would have hurried back to Saint Mary's Hospital, where the Sisters were laboring double shifts every day of the week.

But the work system improved at Saint Mary's. The

first year's records for the hospital showed that more than three hundred patients had been made well again and sent home. The Sisters were encouraged, and they continued to work hard.

Doctor Charlie installed a telephone from the hospital to the Mayos' town offices—and electric bells to call the nurses to the patients' rooms. He also installed an elevator in the shaft that had stood empty since the hospital was built, and thus the Sisters' labors were a little lightened.

There was money now for new furnishings for the rooms—rocking chairs and dressers, pictures and mirrors for the walls. The hospital was in good hands. The Sisters had learned well from Edith Graham, and Sister Joseph was now the head nurse. Furthermore, Mother Alfred had trained other Sisters to take charge. Sisters Hyacinth, Augustine, and Joseph could supervise each shift around the clock.

On "busy" evenings at the hospital, when all three Mayos were in the building to attend patients, they would visit with Mother Alfred in the dining room. "For just a few minutes," Mother Alfred would say. "The Sisters need help in the laundry, but there are some matters to discuss."

"Ah, the family is together again," Doctor Charlie would chuckle.

The old doctor often made the same remark. "Mrs. Mayo says we spend more time here than at home. Well, such is a doctor's life," he added, "and a Mother Superior's."

On one such evening Mother Alfred replied, "There will be others to serve as Sister Superior." She tucked her hands deeper into the folds of her wide Franciscan sleeves and stared at the polished top of the dining room table. "I will be transferred soon. I plan to say little about it—except good-by to my good friends."

The three doctors seemed stunned. Mother Alfred transferred? They had never known the Sisters of Saint Francis without Mother Alfred.

"Where will you go?" old Doctor Mayo asked.

"To Ohio, where Sister Barbara is superior."

"Is she well?"

"Yes, but she is old," Mother Alfred said. "Like me, she will die. God will call us home to Him."

Doctor Charlie looked anxiously at Mother Alfred. "Are you terribly tired, Mother?"

"No more tired than usual, probably." She withdrew her hands from her sleeves and folded them on the table. The hands were rough-skinned, red from the hospital laundry, calloused from shoveling coal. "I am accustomed to hard work," Mother Alfred said. "That is not a reason for leaving," she smiled.

"Perhaps," suggested Doctor Will, "a vacation would be just the thing for you, Mother Alfred."

"Perhaps," she said. "But I feel that my work is finished here. The hospital is built, paid for, and prospering. The future looks assured. The Sisters are doing well. There will be work for them here for more years than I wish to think about. And I believe that the hospital is providing well for the Mayos," she added.

"Splendidly," the old doctor agreed. "Better than our fondest dreams."

Doctor Charlie nodded. "You were right, Mother Alfred."

"In fact," Doctor Will said, "Saint Mary's is almost too successful. The hospital is too small. There should be an addition. Then there would be room for your school of nursing, and for the Sisters to have adequate living quarters."

Mother Alfred smiled wearily. "You must see Mother Matilda about that. She may wish to talk with Sister Joseph, who will be Saint Mary's new superior. As for me, I will say good-by, dear friends. Please give my best to Mrs. Mayo. May God bless you all."

Mother Alfred went back to Ironton, Ohio, where Sister Barbara was in charge of Sacred Heart Institute. Mother Alfred taught catechism and worked around the convent and the chapel.

To Sister Barbara, she said, "It is different when someone else is the superior."

"You mean it is easier?"

"I suppose so. When we were young girls, I always thought that you, my older sister, would be my Sister Superior."

"Perhaps life has worked out that way, after all,"

Sister Barbara said. "I seldom think about such things."

"But I do," smiled Mother Alfred. "Often I think back, remembering days gone by. I used to think back when I was looking ahead! Can you imagine that? But it is true. Sometimes I planned the future on my memory of the past!"

The past, the past. Memories stirred in Mother Alfred's mind, echoing like sounds across the hills and hollows of Luxembourg. But the sounds escaped her and faded away. She had no reason to recapture memories now. Mother Alfred had retired.

Old Doctor Mayo visited her one summer a few years later.

"I was away, Mother Superior, when you came back to Rochester."

"I returned to bury my sister," she explained.

"Yes, I know," he said.

"There is a place next to hers in the convent graveyard," Mother Alfred said gently. "For me, if God will be so kind."

The old doctor looked at her keenly. "Mother Superior, how is your health?"

"I believe you might say it is fair. I have felt pretty well these past few years."

"Would you like to come back to Saint Mary's? I believe it could be arranged. The life would be good for you, Mother Superior. Your hospital has prospered more than I could possibly tell you."

"I know," she said. "Though once the hospital was a burden on the Motherhouse, the Motherhouse can now look to Saint Mary's for support. I would guess that you are looking forward to receiving one thousand patients this year, Doctor Mayo."

"So you have been keeping up on these matters."

"I have friends who write the news to me. Do you remember the little girl whose leg was broken in the tornado—our first patient at the Convent of Saint Francis?"

"Little girl? I don't exactly—"

"You were far too busy that night to remember one person. However, the child and I became friends. She is a novice now with the Sisters of Saint Francis. She may become a teacher, or a nurse. Or she may teach nursing some day."

"I cannot understand," the old doctor told her, "why you hesitate to come back to Saint Mary's."

"Doctor Mayo, you are an intelligent man. Your life has been a struggle against many things—against disease, ignorance, selfishness, greed. My own life has also been a struggle. But I have one privilege that you do not have, Doctor Mayo. I have the privilege of being a Franciscan Sister."

Doctor Mayo pulled at his thick white moustache with his thumb and fore-finger. "Mother Superior, I have never felt sure that I understand this completely. Could we talk about it a moment?"

"I think so, Doctor."

"You Sisters make what is called a vow of poverty. Right?"

"Yes. We embrace poverty. I voluntarily asked for increased poverty each time I took new vows—from Indiana to Minnesota, you might say."

"Then," Doctor Mayo went on, "you spent much of your life struggling against poverty—building schools and convents in the face of hardships. And this is what you did to build Saint Mary's Hospital."

"I welcomed the poverty, Doctor Mayo. We Sisters love poverty for God's glory."

"And now that Saint Mary's—as well as your schools

and convents—can claim some success and prosperity, why can't you enjoy some of the fruits of your labors?"

"That certainly would be all right, Doctor. But there is another vow—that of obedience. In obedience, I do what my superior tells me."

Doctor Mayo rubbed his moustache again. "I'm not sure that I understand yet, Mother Superior. But I am satisfied that you do not object to the prosperity that we have found in Rochester. Everything is going wonderfully there. We are even becoming famous! Specialists from the East and from Europe call Saint Mary's the 'clinic in the cornfields.' The experts come to watch Doctor Will and Doctor Charlie do their operations. And the antiseptics—a marvelous success."

"I know, Doctor Mayo. I have been kept informed, even about the additions to Saint Mary's. The hospital will grow and grow."

"Then it is not the success that keeps you away? Somehow I had an idea that you must have poverty to spur you on—to struggle against."

Mother Alfred shrugged her shoulders. "The good things of life are given by the Lord, as well as the trials. You see, Doctor, I had wealth from my inheritance. I had no objection to receiving that money," she smiled. "I just tried to do good with it."

"You did succeed, Mother Superior. I wish that you could return to Rochester. We are growing fast and could use your help."

"Well, the Mother General seems to want me to stay here," she told Doctor Mayo. "Please try to understand."

"I will try." It was the best Doctor Mayo could do.

On a summer day in the year 1906, old Doctor Mayo sat on a back porch of Saint Mary's Hospital, across the lawn from the wooded hills that looked down upon Rochester. With him was Doctor Ernest Hall from British Columbia, who was writing an article about medicine for the *Canada Lancet*. Doctor Hall had a notebook and pencil in his hands.

"Now, when you write this story," Doctor Mayo told Doctor Hall, "be careful not to brag about the Mayos. Doctor Will and Doctor Charlie are very particular about this. No cheap publicity, please."

"Certainly, Doctor Mayo. I will merely report the facts. For example, last year, in 1905, there were more surgical cases at Saint Mary's than at any other hospital in the United States—more than Johns Hopkins."

"Yes, that is correct," Doctor Mayo said.

"Doctor Mayo, what can you tell me about this nun, Mother Alfred, who started this hospital?"

"Mother Alfred? I always called her 'Mother Superior.' It seemed to fit her. She was a superior person—so full of hope and energy. She was an optimist. Nothing seemed to discourage her. She loved a challenge. And she knew her job. A wonderful woman, Mother Alfred."

"Go on," Doctor Hall nodded.

"She has been dead seven years. But her predictions about Saint Mary's were realized before she died. Twenty years ago she told me that the hospital would have patients from far and wide, and that Doctor Will and Doctor Charlie would be grateful for this chance to practice the newest and the best in medicine. All of this has come to pass."

"Did Mother Alfred build other hospitals besides Saint Mary's?"

"None. Many schools and convents, but just this one hospital. And soon after she got Saint Mary's in order, she was transferred to Ohio, where the Sisters had a school and a farm. Later she was sent to Saint Paul. She died there in 1899, at Saint Joseph's Hospital. She was seventy-one."

"What did she die of, Doctor?"

"A rupture. I suppose she had injured herself years before. Maybe working or lifting coal as she did. But she told nobody."

"Could surgery at Saint Mary's have saved her life?"

"Probably not. That operation is now easy, but a few years ago the mortality was high. I am sure that she knew that. She knew so much. A tremendous intelligence. You know, that was one of the most amazing things about Mother Alfred—her intelligence."

"How's that, Doctor Mayo?"

"She was a teacher. She built schools and selected

teachers and put them to work 'instructing youth,' as she called it. In the same way she built Saint Mary's, selected Sisters for the work."

"Just like that?" Doctor Hall asked.

"Almost. She had to talk me into the idea of the hospital. I was her chief of staff at the start. But she was not at all surprised to see Saint Mary's grow from a hospital into a clinic here in the cornfields. She expected it to happen. I think she expected Saint Mary's to become the biggest hospital of its kind in the whole world. A remarkable intellect!"

"Did you really expect this medical center to fail, Doctor Mayo?"

"Well, I remember her argument. I told her a hospital would not succeed because nobody within one hundred miles had wanted one enough to build it and make it work. But Mother Alfred reasoned that a hospital would succeed *because* it was the only one within one hundred miles and because it was needed—far beyond those hundred miles. She was right."

Doctor Hall closed his notebook. "Thank you, Doctor Mayo. I believe that I have enough material for my article."

"You are welcome, Doctor. Tell me, what do you propose to call your article? Have you a title yet?"

"I think so, Doctor Mayo. I plan to call my story 'Echoes From Saint Mary's Clinic.' How does that strike you?"

"Fair enough. That's what you have here. Echoes."

Doctor Hall wrote, "This clinic, visitors say, surpasses anything on the other side of the Atlantic."

That would have pleased Mother Alfred.

"Fair enough. That's what you have here, Echoes," Doctor Hall wrote. "This clinic, visitors say, surpasses anything on the other side of the Atlantic."

That would have pleased Mother Alfred.

SPANISH FLAG
1492

PERSONAL BANNER OF COLUMBUS

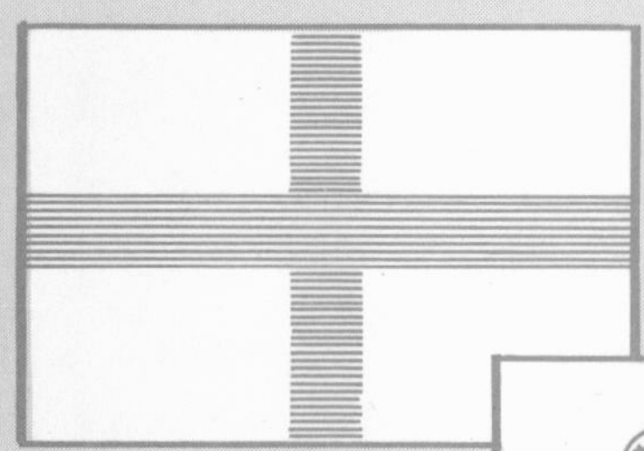

CROSS OF ST. GEORGE
JOHN CABOT
1497

PAPAL BANNER

FLAG OF FRANCE
JACQUES CARTIER
1534

FLAG OF
HUDSON
1607

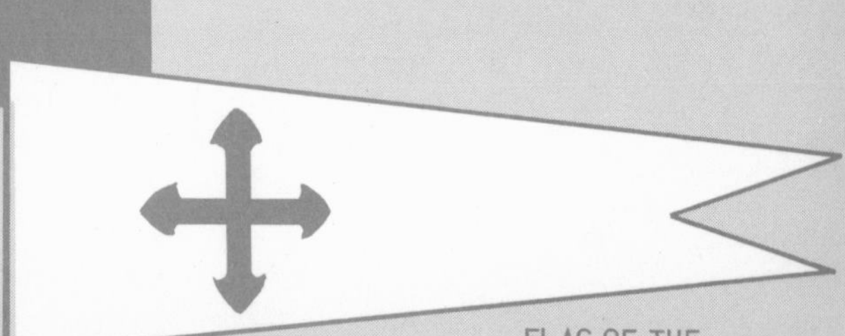

FLAG OF THE
CRUSADES